Countryside Lover's Puzzle & Quiz Book

Countryside Lover's Puzzle & Quiz Book

Over 230 themed puzzles, including arrowords, codewords, crosswords, wordfits, and over 30 quizzes

AURA

This edition published in 2010
by Baker & Taylor (UK) Limited,
Bicester, Oxfordshire

Puzzles copyright © 2010 Puzzle Press Limited

Copyright © 2010 Arcturus Publishing Limited
26/27 Bickels Yard, 151–153 Bermondsey Street
London SE1 3HA

ISBN: 978-1-90723-109-4

AD001581EN

Printed in Germany

INTRODUCTION

The puzzles and quizzes presented in
the *Countryside Lover's Puzzle & Quiz
Book* have been specially devised to
present an entertaining variety of puzzles
with a natural flavour.

Whatever your taste in puzzles and
quizzes, we are sure you will find this
selection challenging and fun.

Solutions to all of the puzzles can be
found at the back of the book, but try not
to peek!

Watery Wordfit

Fit the listed English lakes and reservoirs into the grid below, then rearrange the letters in the shaded squares to form the name of another English lake or reservoir.

4 letters
CHEW
HURY

5 letters
DELPH
DRIFT
HANCH
OLTON
SLADE
WAYOH

6 letters
CROWDY
DINGLE
NASEBY

7 letters
BLAGDON

8 letters
ABBERTON
COW GREEN
DALE DYKE

9 letters
WINDLEDEN

10 letters
GREENBOOTH

12 letters
ORCHARDLEIGH

2 Sheep Wordsearch

Find the listed breeds of sheep hidden in the grid below.
Words run in either a forward or backward direction,
horizontally, vertically or diagonally, but always in a straight line.

```
A W B D L O W S T O C G H
U T E L P T I I F K U R E
D T Q N L S U N T T O A R
F O Z O S E P U E M N K D
L C E A D L Y T A A L K W
L R W S O V E N D E E N I
I A O C R S O Y X P X O C
H A M H P V U C D A E L K
Y W A E E N K N Y A T A M
R M S V R Q F R R U L M A
R P H I D I A H U A T E S
E R A O L S N O D K X U A
K U M T A T Q O U M T H I
```

ARCOTT	HERDWICK	ROMANOV
AWASSI	KERRY HILL	RYA
CHEVIOT	LLEYN	SOAY
COTSWOLD	LONK	TEXEL
DALA	MASAI	TUNIS
DORPER	MASHAM	VENDEEN
GUTE	MERINO	WENSLEYDALE

Honeycomb

Place the letters of each word, one per cell, so that every word flows in a clockwise direction around a number.

Where the hexagons of one word overlap with those of another, the letter in each cell is common to both.

When finished, rearrange the letters in the pale green hexagons to form the name of a tree.

APLOMB

COUNTY

EXPIRE

EXTEND

HATRED

HIDDEN

IDIOCY

MOROSE

PARIAH

RESCUE

TRIPLE

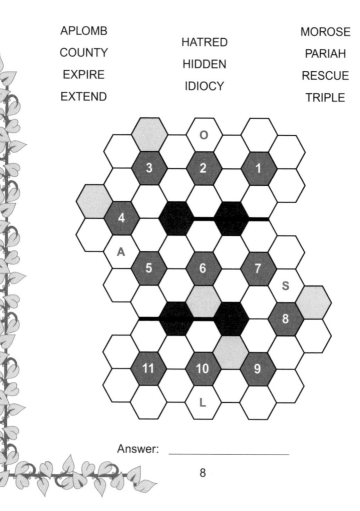

Answer: _____

Codeword

4

Every letter in this crossword has been replaced by a number, the number remaining the same for that letter wherever it occurs. Can you substitute numbers for letters and complete the crossword? One word has already been entered into the grid, to help you on your way.

When finished, use the code to spell out a type of butterfly.

A	21	23	3	3	8	7		11	4	8	8	1	18
B	5		7			15		17		23		6	
C	26	7	21	20		9	17	7	9	4	17	7	10
D	9		25	4	13	7		4		17	7	10	1
E	4		8		8		25			18		6	
F	25	4	8	1	18		16	8	4	25	25	7	18
G	20		4		14	1	5			4		20	
H	7	22	24	23	18	1	15		20	4	8	2	7
I	25		18			8		21		25		4	
J	23	18	19	20		25		9	17	1	10		17
								P	R	O	D		
K	19	1	20	7	21	23	2	7		26	7	8	25
L		25		17		18		18			19		7
M	12	7	8	1	18	11		10	1	19	13	7	10

Letters down the sides: N O P Q R S T U V W X Y Z

1	2	3	4	5	6	7	8	9	10	11	12	13
O								P	D			

14	15	16	17	18	19	20	21	22	23	24	25	26
			R									

Answer

26	1	18	4	17	19	20

9

Wordladder

5

Change one letter at a time (but not the position of any letter) to make a new word – and move from the word at the top of the ladder to the word at the bottom using the exact number of rungs provided.

F I S H

F O W L

True or False

6

Can you decide whether the statement below is true or false?

The Edible Dormouse, otherwise known as the Fat Dormouse (*Glis glis*), is the only dormouse native to the British Isles.

True or False

Petal Puzzle

How many words of three or more letters can you make from those on the petals, without using plurals, abbreviations or proper nouns? The central letter must appear once in every word and no letter may be used more than once unless it is on a different petal. There is at least one nine-letter word to be found.

8 Forested Areas

Fit the letters F, O, R, E, S and T into the grid in such a way that each horizontal row, each vertical column and each of the heavily outlined sections of six squares contains a different letter. Some letters are already in place.

	F				
					E
				S	
			T		
	O		R		

9 Animal Tracker

Starting at the top left corner and ending at the bottom right, track a path from letter to letter, in any direction except diagonally, in order to find the hidden animals. All of the letters must be used once only.

C	O	T	A	M	U	S	S	Q	U	N	G	A	R	O	E	M
H	P	P	I	F	F	A	R	I	I	A	K	X	O	O	L	U
I	O	P	H	E	A	B	T	G	R	R	E	L	F	R	D	R
P	M	U	N	K	R	B	I	U	O	M	L	B	E	A	E	E
W	K	R	A	V	D	A	E	S	L	O	I	B	R	E	G	R
E	E	L	G	E	R	A	X	C	E	T	R	H	N	A	R	S
A	S	T	I	R	L	Y	N	A	M	T	E	Y	E	H	O	E

12

10 Anagram Mountain

Correctly solve the anagrams each step of the way from the top to the bottom of the mountain and the name of a plant or animal will be revealed in the central column of bricks.

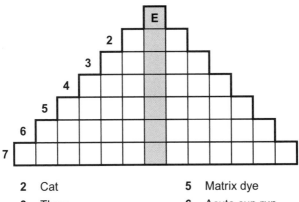

2	Cat	5	Matrix dye
3	Three	6	Acute cup run
4	Etna pit	7	In mean compact

11 Spelling Bee

Which is the only one of the following to be correctly spelled?

a   FRITTILLARY

b   FRITTILARY

c   FRITILLARY

d   FRITILARY

12 Natural Selection

Find the correct answer to each question from the four alternatives.

1 What kind of creatures live in an apiary?
- **a.** Wasps
- **b.** Bees
- **c.** Birds
- **d.** Chimpanzees

2 What term describes a creature or plant that is both male and female?
- **a.** Bisexual
- **b.** Herbivore
- **c.** Hermaphrodite
- **d.** Bi-gender

3 What is the common term for the flittermouse?
- **a.** Bat
- **b.** Wren
- **c.** Brown rat
- **d.** Sparrow

4 What is the better-known name of the fruit physalis?
- **a.** Kiwi
- **b.** Kumquat
- **c.** Star fruit
- **d.** Cape gooseberry

5 What is the common name for the tree genus salix?
- **a.** Ash
- **b.** Willow
- **c.** Beech
- **d.** Oak

6 Which 'greenhouse' gas is absorbed by trees?
- **a.** Carbon dioxide
- **b.** Ozone
- **c.** Nitrogen
- **d.** Carbon monoxide

7 Cetology is the study of which group of animals?
- **a.** Birds
- **b.** Whales and dolphins
- **c.** Freshwater molluscs
- **d.** Cats

8 Lepidoptera is the term for which order of insects?
- **a.** Termites
- **b.** Spiders
- **c.** Flies
- **d.** Butterflies and moths

13 Keyword Crossword

Solve the crossword puzzle in the usual way, then rearrange the letters in the shaded squares to spell out a keyword: the name of a creature.

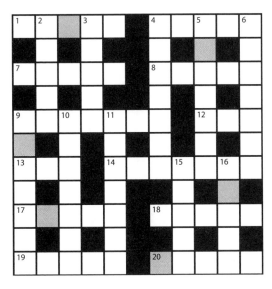

Across

- **1** Greta ___, film star (5)
- **4** Woolly mammals (5)
- **7** Grinding tooth (5)
- **8** Relish served with food (5)
- **9** Quantity (7)
- **12** Expert (3)
- **13** Fish eggs (3)
- **14** Ask earnestly (7)
- **17** Become less intense (5)
- **18** Adult female (5)
- **19** Item of clothing (5)
- **20** Make up for (5)

Down

- **2** Love intensely (5)
- **3** Alloy of copper and zinc (5)
- **4** Believe to be true (7)
- **5** Teach (7)
- **6** Fictitious reason (7)
- **9** Imaginary water nymph (7)
- **10** Unexceptional (7)
- **11** Devoid of practical purpose (7)
- **15** Fowl's perch (5)
- **16** Once more (5)

Whirlpool

Find a route for the fish to take in order to escape from the middle of the whirlpool to the calmer waters beyond.

National Park Sudoku

Every row, every column and each of the nine smaller boxes of nine squares should be filled with a different number from 1 to 9 inclusive. Some numbers are already in place. When the grid is completely filled, decode the numbers in the shaded squares to spell out the name of a national park. Every row should be read from left to right, starting from the top and working to the bottom of the grid.

	5	9		1				4
					5		8	
			2		3	9		5
7						5		6
	6						9	
4		8						7
3		7	1		8			
	2		6					
5				2		1	4	

Code

1	2	3	4	5	6	7	8	9
I	G	M	R	N	A	C	S	O

Answer: _____

17

Shape-up

Every row and column in this grid originally contained one bird, one flower, one leaf, one mushroom and two blank squares, although not necessarily in that order. Every symbol with a black arrow refers to the first of the four symbols encountered in the direction of the arrow. Every symbol with a white arrow refers to the second of the four symbols encountered in the direction of the arrow. Can you complete the original grid?

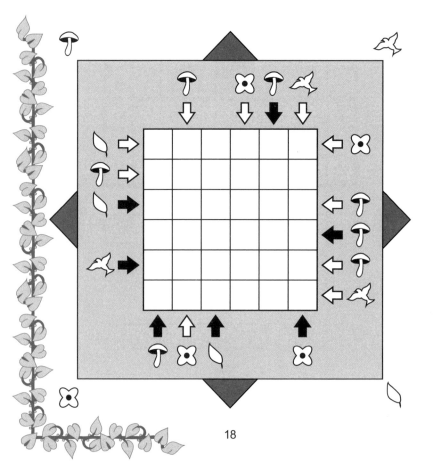

17 Round Dozen

First solve the clues. All of the solutions end with the letter in the middle of the circle, and in every word an additional letter is in place. When the puzzle is complete, you can then go on to discover two birds, reading clockwise around the green ring of letters.

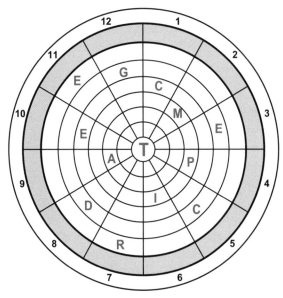

1 Businessperson engaged in retail trade (8)

2 Disagreement (8)

3 Largest of its kind (8)

4 Outlook (8)

5 Episode (8)

6 Vision (8)

7 Slope (8)

8 Aromatic (8)

9 Inhabitant (8)

10 Charge less than the opposition (8)

11 Police or army officer (8)

12 Alternative name for the aubergine (8)

Answer: _____ and _____

18 Natural Selection

Find the correct answer to each question from the four alternatives.

1 Which is the world's largest web-footed bird?
a. Albatross
b. Great auk
c. Great frigatebird
d. Great crested cormorant

2 Which plant's name translates from the Italian for 'beautiful woman'?
a. Begonia
b. Bellis
c. Belladonna
d. Amaryllis

3 How many wings has a honey-bee?
a. Eight
b. Two
c. Six
d. Four

4 From which crop plant is linseed oil derived?
a. Rapeseed
b. Cotton
c. Flax
d. Maize

5 Which Swedish naturalist and botanist (1707-1778) invented the modern system of defining all living things using two Latin names?
a. Nobel
b. Linnaeus
c. Zetterstedt
d. Bjorling

6 Which material, used in ornament and jewellery making, is fossilised wood resin?
a. Peridot
b. Jet
c. Amethyst
d. Amber

7 The largest diversity of species on Earth is to be found where?
a. The Amazon rainforest
b. Central Africa
c. The Indian subcontinent
d. Australasia

8 What kind of creature is a manatee?
a. Freshwater fish
b. Marine mammal
c. Snake
d. South American marsupial

19 Pine Forest

The object of this puzzle is to trace a single path from the top left square to the bottom right square of the grid, moving through all of the cells in either a horizontal, vertical or diagonal direction. Every cell must be entered once only and your path should take you through the letters in the sequence P-I-N-E-P-I-N-E, etc. Can you find the logical way through?

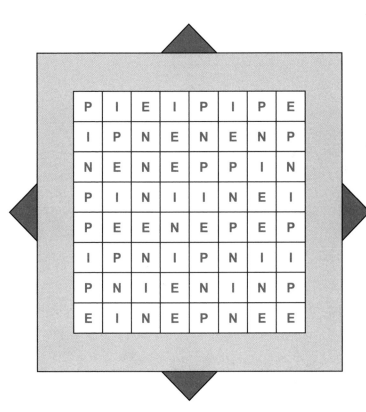

P	I	E	I	P	I	P	E
I	P	N	E	N	E	N	P
N	E	N	E	P	P	I	N
P	I	N	I	I	N	E	I
P	E	E	N	E	P	E	P
I	P	N	I	P	N	I	I
P	N	I	E	N	I	N	P
E	I	N	E	P	N	E	E

What's It Worth?

Each symbol stands for a different number. In order to reach the correct total at the end of each row and column, what is the value of the bat, frog, rabbit and starfish?

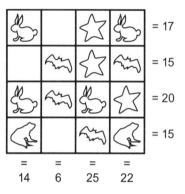

Shape Spotter

Which is the only shape to appear twice in exactly the same shading (black, white or green) in the box below? You'll need a keen eye for this one, as some shapes overlap others!

22 Riddle-Me-Ree

Find one letter per line, following the clues given in the verse below. For example, 'My first is in houses, but never in homes' gives the letter U as the first letter. When you have finished, the letters will spell another word.

My first is in POETRY, and also in RHYME,

My second's not in YOURS, but is found in MINE,

My third is in COVER, although not in HIDE,

My fourth's not in BROAD, but is found in WIDE,

My fifth is in DRONE, but not found in BEE,

My whole can be seen on its way to the sea.

1st	2nd	3rd	4th	5th

23 True or False

Can you decide whether the statement below is true or false?

The gestation period of the elephant is 22 months, the longest of any land animal.

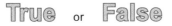

Telephone Code

Use the telephone dial in order to spell out a quotation attributed to Charles Darwin.

4 8   4 8   6 6 8   8 4 3   8 8 7 6 6 3 3 8 8   6 3   8 4 3

8 6 3 2 4 3 8   8 4 1 8   8 9 7 9 4 9 3 8 ,   6 6 7   8 4 3

5 6 8 8   4 6 8 3 5 5 4 3 3 6 8   8 4 1 8   8 9 7 9 4 9 3 8 .

4 8   4 8   8 4 3   6 6 3   8 4 1 8   4 8   8 4 3   5 6 8 8

1 2 1 6 8 1 1 5 3   8 6   2 4 1 6 3 3 .

25

NNR Arroword

Place the answers in the direction shown by the arrows for each clue. When finished, the letters in the green squares spell out the name of a National Nature Reserve in Pembrokeshire, reading from top left to bottom right.

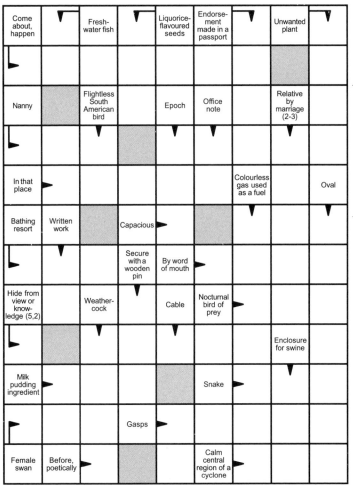

Mix 'n' Match

Pair up each of the boxes below to form the names of eight different trees.

LOW

RCH

BLACK

THORN

PL

LAR

POP

BEAM

SYCA

ANE

WIL

WAL

NUT

MORE

HORN

BI

<table>
<tr><td></td><td></td><td></td><td></td></tr>
</table>

27 Round the Block

You won't need a starting block to get you under way, because it isn't a race! Just arrange the six-letter solutions to the clues into the six blocks around each clue number. Write the answers in a clockwise or anticlockwise direction and you'll find that the last answer fits into the first; the main problem will be to decide in which square to put the first letter of each word…

When read in a clockwise direction (not necessarily starting at either of the topmost squares), the letters in the pale green squares spell out the name of a bird.

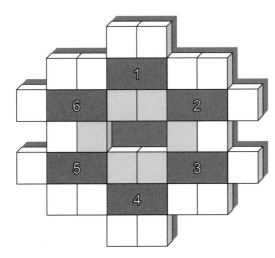

1 Bending down in deference before a monarch

2 Common spice, *Zingiber officinale*

3 Country house

4 Common citrus fruit

5 Source, beginning

6 Having possession of

Casting Shadows

Which one of the shadows is that of the eagle shown here?

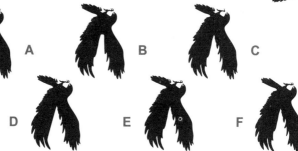

A   B   C

D   E   F

The Bottom Line

The bottom line of this grid is waiting to be filled. Every square in the solution contains only one symbol from rows 1 to 5 above, although two or more squares in the solution may contain the same symbol. At the end of every numbered row is a score, which shows:

1. the number of symbols placed in the correct finishing position on the bottom line, as indicated by a tick; and

2. the number of symbols which appear on the bottom line, but in a different position, as indicated by a cross.

Can you fill each square with the correct symbol?

				Score
1	🕷	🐸	🦅	🍄	X
2	🦢	🦅	🍃	🕷	X
3	🍄	🍄	🕷	🐸	X
4	🐰	🦅	🦅	🍃	X
5	🐸	🐰	🍄	🦅	X X
					✓✓✓✓

28

Spidoku

Each of the eight segments of the spider's web should be filled with a different number from 1 to 8, in such a way that every ring also contains a different number from 1 to 8.
The segments run from the outside of the spider's web to the centre, and the rings run all the way around.
Some numbers are already in place. Can you fill in the rest?

29

Wordfit

Fit the listed mountains into the grid below, then rearrange the letters in the shaded squares to form the name of another mountain.

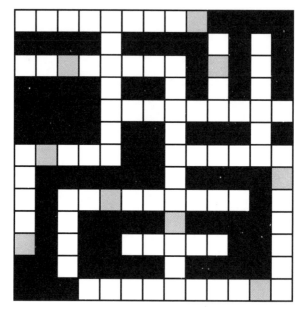

4 letters
FUJI
MERU

5 letters
KAMET
KENYA
TEIDE

6 letters
ELBRUS
MAKALU

7 letters
EVEREST
SNOWDON

8 letters
BEN NEVIS

9 letters
EL CAPITAN
MONT BLANC
MONTE ROSA

10 letters
MATTERHORN

11 letters
SCAFELL PIKE

Rivers Wordsearch

32

Find the listed rivers hidden in the grid below. Words run in either a forward or backward direction, horizontally, vertically or diagonally, but always in a straight line.

D	I	R	U	O	S	S	I	M	J	N	S	Q
V	O	L	G	A	I	X	E	O	R	E	G	E
E	Q	G	Z	R	M	T	R	L	T	X	Z	K
K	N	Z	G	C	N	D	H	A	I	T	M	R
A	K	I	Y	N	A	H	R	A	G	N	I	W
L	T	H	H	N	D	H	D	N	M	O	S	S
U	G	U	Q	R	P	T	A	A	G	E	H	Z
T	A	A	M	U	G	Y	A	R	N	A	S	A
S	V	N	E	R	Z	I	A	N	N	U	D	M
I	M	G	E	Q	L	N	O	N	D	D	B	B
V	P	H	X	L	D	C	O	N	G	O	G	E
P	X	O	Q	E	T	N	I	O	I	B	K	Z
E	G	N	A	R	O	N	O	Z	A	M	A	I

AMAZON	LENA	SHANNON
CONGO	MISSOURI	THAMES
DANUBE	NILE	TIGRIS
EUPHRATES	ORANGE	VISTULA
HUANG HO	RHINE	VOLGA
INDUS	RIO GRANDE	YANGTZE
JORDAN		ZAMBEZI

31

Honeycomb

Place the letters of each word, one per cell, so that every word flows in a clockwise direction around a number.

Where the hexagons of one word overlap with those of another, the letter in each cell is common to both.

When finished, rearrange the letters in the pale green hexagons to form the name of a plant.

BREATH

CANOPY

HARROW

KARATE

MATRON

MORBID

SNEAKY

SULTAN

TAILOR

TATTOO

TOMCAT

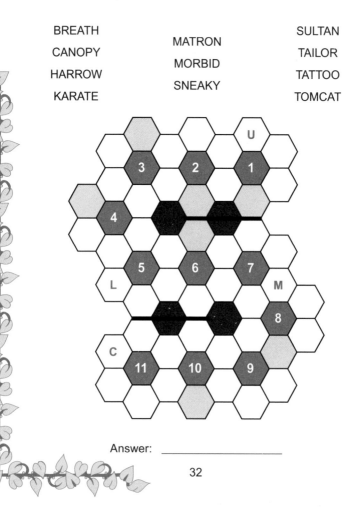

Answer: _____

34 Codeword

Every letter in this crossword has been replaced by a number, the number remaining the same for that letter wherever it occurs. Can you substitute numbers for letters and complete the crossword? One word has already been entered into the grid, to help you on your way.
When finished, use the code to spell out a plant.

A	4	13	26	13	■	23	19	14	26	6	12	14	2	N
B	13	■	19	■	3	■	26	■	5	■	17	■	14	O
C	8	19	17	5	17	9	16	■	8	17	5	21	26	P
D	24	■	13	■	1	■	25	■	12	■	4	9	9	Q
E	2	22	26	19	10	■	26	15	26	5	14	26	■	R
F	14	■	■	■	24	19	16	14	■	■	20	8	26	S
G	9	■	26	7	5	14	■	19	24	9	25	■	16	T
H	25	4 I	9	■	■	4	6	17	9	■	■	■	16	U
I	■	2 D	17	13	4	9	17	■	8	17	20	14	19	V
J	25	17 O	9	■	2	■	24	■	5	■	8	■	4	W
K	20	5 L	1	5	1	■	20	18	24	14	14	15	14	X
L	26	■	13	■	5	■	4	■	16	■	14	■	11	Y
M	19	24	20	25	5	4	9	16	■	4	2	5	14	Z

1	2 D	3	4 I	5 L	6	7	8	9	10	11	12	13
14	15	16	17 O	18	19	20	21	22	23	24	25	26

Answer

20	17	26	8	22	17	19	25

35 Wordladder

Change one letter at a time (but not the position of any letter) to make a new word – and move from the word at the top of the ladder to the word at the bottom using the exact number of rungs provided.

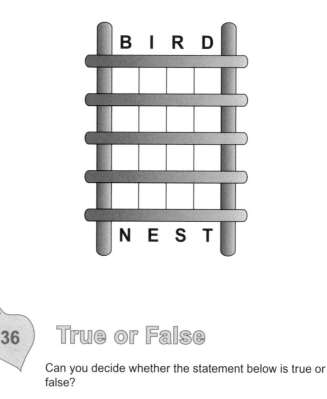

B I R D

N E S T

36 True or False

Can you decide whether the statement below is true or false?

The patches of colour on horse chestnut flowers turn from yellow to red with age.

True or False

34

Petal Puzzle

How many words of three or more letters can you make from those on the petals, without using plurals, abbreviations or proper nouns? The central letter must appear once in every word and no letter may be used more than once unless it is on a different petal. There is at least one nine-letter word to be found.

38 Forested Areas

Fit the letters F, O, R, E, S and T into the grid in such a way that each horizontal row, each vertical column and each of the heavily outlined sections of six squares contains a different letter. Some letters are already in place.

				E	F
		T			S
O	R				

39 Geographical Tracker

Starting at the top left corner and ending at the bottom right, track a path from letter to letter, in any direction except diagonally, in order to find the hidden geographical features. All of the letters must be used once only.

M	N	P	R	A	I	R	S	P	R	E	Y	S	E	R	S	S
O	I	A	I	H	E	I	T	N	I	G	Y	R	A	F	I	U
U	N	T	L	E	S	E	R	G	G	E	A	U	U	T	S	R
L	A	F	L	D	W	E	G	R	O	T	A	M	O	O	E	E
L	T	R	E	T	A	P	V	O	L	C	L	A	V	R	N	S
N	U	R	I	R	S	M	A	W	S	A	P	L	Y	P	I	E
D	R	A	V	E	T	R	E	A	M	N	O	L	E	L	A	A

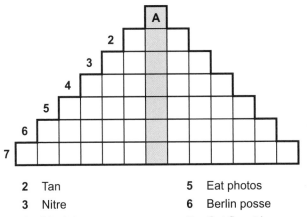

40 Anagram Mountain

Correctly solve the anagrams each step of the way from the top to the bottom of the mountain and the name of a plant or animal will be revealed in the central column of bricks.

| | | | | | A | | | | | |

2 Tan
3 Nitre
4 Mock ham

5 Eat photos
6 Berlin posse
7 Got fluent bear

41 Spelling Bee

Which is the only one of the following to be correctly spelled?

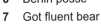

a   STICHWORT

b   STICHWERT

c   STITCHWERT

d   STITCHWORT

Natural Selection

Find the correct answer to each question from the four alternatives.

1 What term is used to classify animals that eat both animal and vegetable food?
   a. Carnivorous   **b.** Omnivorous
   c. Herbivorous   **d.** Insectivorous

2 What is the correct name for the buffalo of North America?
   a. Caribou   **b.** Reindeer
   c. Elk   **d.** Bison

3 Which animal provides us with a 'chammy' leather?
   a. Chamise   **b.** Chamale
   c. Chamois   **d.** Champiogne

4 Which southern African animal's name translates as 'earth-pig'?
   a. Aardvark   **b.** Boomslang
   c. Dik-dik   **d.** Armadillo

5 What is the proper name of the now-extinct European wild ox?
   a. Barochs   **b.** Aurochs
   c. Bovox   **d.** Mooselk

6 Which constellation is in the shape of a slightly flattened 'W'?
   a. Taurus   **b.** Aries
   c. Leo   **d.** Cassiopeia

7 What name is given to the epoch covering the last ice age?
   a. Pleistocene   **b.** Jurassic
   c. Cretaceous   **d.** Devonian

8 How does the German-named dachshund translate into English?
   a. Roof dog   **b.** Hunter hound
   c. Badger dog   **d.** Low hound

Keyword Crossword

Solve the crossword puzzle in the usual way, then rearrange the letters in the shaded squares to spell out a keyword: the name of a creature.

Across

3 Tubes (5)
6 At a more distant point (7)
7 Diversion requiring physical exertion (5)
10 Atmosphere (3)
11 Fragrant garden flowers (5)
12 Catch sight of (3)
13 Of a thing (3)
14 Period approaching an election (3,2)
15 Took in solid food (3)
16 Expand abnormally (5)
19 US state (7)
20 Tiny (5)

Down

1 Live in a tent (4)
2 Agitate (4)
3 Arm exercises performed lying face to the floor (5-3)
4 Animal or plant that lives in or on a host (8)
5 Trousers that end above the knee (6)
8 Short musical drama (8)
9 Calm (8)
12 Shelters from light (6)
17 Impulse (4)
18 Come to earth (4)

Whirlpool

Find a route for the fish to take in order to escape from the middle of the whirlpool to the calmer waters beyond.

Plant Sudoku

45

Every row, every column and each of the nine smaller boxes of nine squares should be filled with a different number from 1 to 9 inclusive. Some numbers are already in place. When the grid is completely filled, decode the numbers in the shaded squares to spell out the name of a plant. Every row should be read from left to right, starting from the top and working to the bottom of the grid.

		1	4		8		3	6
	2			6	9			
		4	6			8	5	2
6	9	5				7	4	
			7	4			8	
7	6		3			2	1	

Code

1	2	3	4	5	6	7	8	9
N	S	K	M	T	H	D	E	O

Answer: _____

41

46 Shape-up

Every row and column in this grid originally contained one bird, one flower, one leaf, one mushroom and two blank squares, although not necessarily in that order. Every symbol with a black arrow refers to the first of the four symbols encountered in the direction of the arrow. Every symbol with a white arrow refers to the second of the four symbols encountered in the direction of the arrow. Can you complete the original grid?

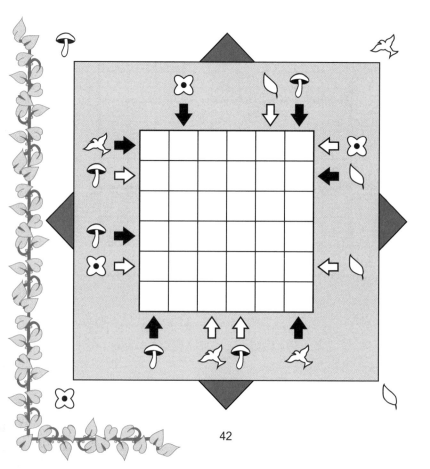

42

Round Dozen

47

First solve the clues. All of the solutions end with the letter in the middle of the circle, and in every word an additional letter is in place. When the puzzle is complete, you can then go on to discover two insects, reading clockwise around the green ring of letters.

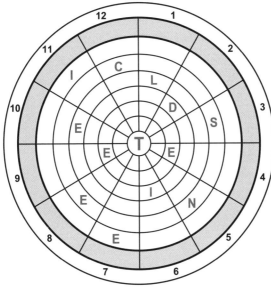

1 Precisely and clearly expressed

2 Plentiful

3 Someone who lives at a particular place

4 Most strikingly odd or unusual

5 Lacking general education or knowledge

6 Slope

7 Salad vegetable

8 Indian or African animal

9 First

10 Accepting

11 Maritime rescue vessel

12 Edible terrestrial snail

Answer: _____ and _____

Find the correct answer to each question from the four alternatives.

1 Of which order of mammal is the lemming?
a. Rodent   **b.** Carnivore
c. Chiroptera   **d.** Marsupial

2 What is the name for a young hare?
a. Harelet   **b.** Leveret
c. Loppet   **d.** Kitten

3 Which is the only continent not to have reptiles?
a. Europe   **b.** South America
c. Australia   **d.** Antarctica

4 Which fish is the world's most poisonous?
a. Stonefish   **b.** Arctic char
c. Weaver fish   **d.** Scorpion fish

5 Which is Britain's only native poisonous snake?
a. Slow snake   **b.** Grass snake
c. Adder   **d.** Green snake

6 What is the term for a female rabbit?
a. Doe   **b.** Mare
c. Queen   **d.** Ewe

7 What is the southern equivalent of the Aurora Borealis?
a. Aurora Frigidis   **b.** Aurora Antarctis
c. Aurora Australis   **d.** Aurora Polaris

8 A Sealyham is a breed of which type of dog?
a. Spaniel   **b.** Terrier
c. Foxhound   **d.** Retriever

49 Pine Forest

The object of this puzzle is to trace a single path from the top left square to the bottom right square of the grid, moving through all of the cells in either a horizontal, vertical or diagonal direction. Every cell must be entered once only and your path should take you through the letters in the sequence P-I-N-E-P-I-N-E, etc. Can you find the logical way through?

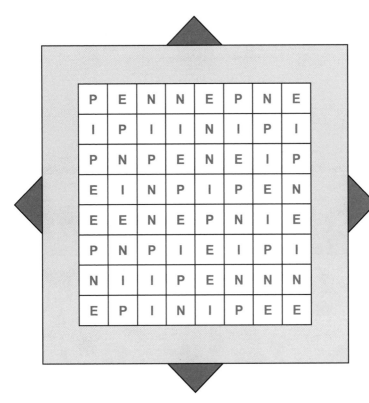

P	E	N	N	E	P	N	E
I	P	I	I	N	I	P	I
P	N	P	E	N	E	I	P
E	I	N	P	I	P	E	N
E	E	N	E	P	N	I	E
P	N	P	I	E	I	P	I
N	I	I	P	E	N	N	N
E	P	I	N	I	P	E	E

What's It Worth?

Each symbol stands for a different number. In order to reach the correct total at the end of each row and column, what is the value of the bat, frog, rabbit and starfish?

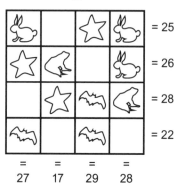

Shape Spotter

Which is the only shape to appear twice in exactly the same shading (black, white or green) in the box below? You'll need a keen eye for this one, as some shapes overlap others!

52   Riddle-Me-Ree

Find one letter per line, following the clues given in the verse below. For example, 'My first is in houses, but never in homes' gives the letter U as the first letter. When you have finished, the letters will spell another word.

My first is in DOUBLE, and also in TREBLE,

My second's in STONE, as well as in PEBBLE,

My third's found in APPLE, but never in PLUM,

My fourth's not in BREAD, though it is seen in CRUMB,

My fifth's not in BONNET, but is found in HOOD,

My whole is a tree that you'd see in a wood.

1st	2nd	3rd	4th	5th

53   True or False

Can you decide whether the statement below is true or false?

A clingfish clamps itself to the underside of a rock by means of a suction disc on its belly.

True   or   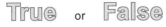 False

Telephone Code

Use the telephone dial in order to spell out a quotation attributed to George Montagu, ornithologist.

4 8　　4 8　　3 0 6 3 7 4 5 3 6 8 1 5 5 0

4 6 6 9 6　　8 4 1 8　　1 4 7 2 8　　2 6　　6 6 8

4 6 8 8 4 6 2 8 4 9 3 5 0　　4 6 6 9　　8 4 3

2 9 7 1 8 4 6 6　　6 3　　8 4 3 4 7　　6 9 6

4 6 2 9 1 1 8 4 6 6

55 NNR Arroword

Place the answers in the direction shown by the arrows for each clue. When finished, the letters in the green squares can be rearranged to spell out the name of a National Nature Reserve in Argyll and Bute.

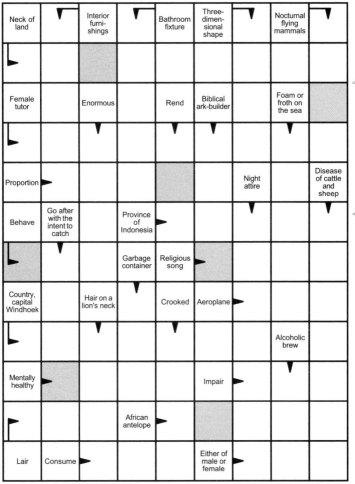

56 Mix 'n' Match

Pair up each of the boxes below to form the names of eight different flowers.

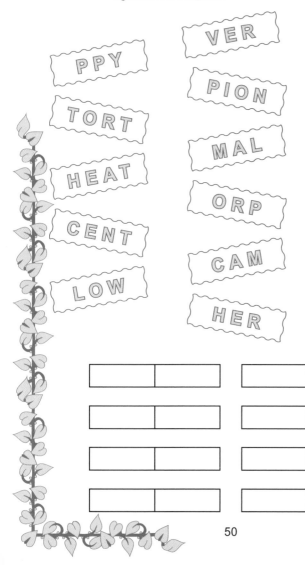

PPY

VER

INE

TORT

PION

AURY

HEAT

MAL

CLO

CENT

ORP

BIS

LOW

CAM

PO

HER

50

57 Round the Block

You won't need a starting block to get you under way, because it isn't a race! Just arrange the six-letter solutions to the clues into the six blocks around each clue number. Write the answers in a clockwise or anticlockwise direction and you'll find that the last answer fits into the first; the main problem will be to decide in which square to put the first letter of each word…

When read in a clockwise direction (not necessarily starting at either of the topmost squares), the letters in the pale green squares spell out the name of a part of a flower.

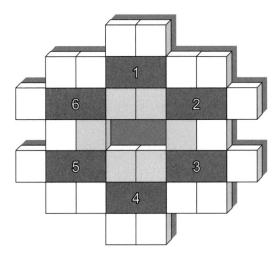

1 Warming device

2 Rivulet

3 Burrowing animal

4 Popular fruit

5 City, the capital of Iran

6 Monarch's seat

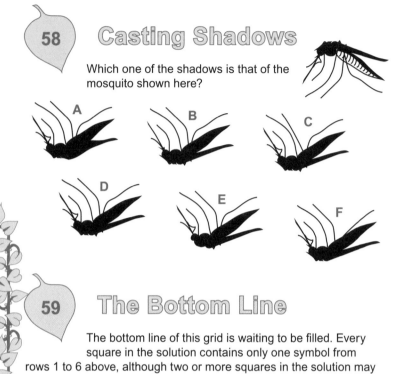

58 Casting Shadows

Which one of the shadows is that of the mosquito shown here?

A

B

C

D

E

F

59 The Bottom Line

The bottom line of this grid is waiting to be filled. Every square in the solution contains only one symbol from rows 1 to 6 above, although two or more squares in the solution may contain the same symbol. At the end of every numbered row is a score, which shows:

1 the number of symbols placed in the correct finishing position on the bottom line, as indicated by a tick; and

2 the number of symbols which appear on the bottom line, but in a different position, as indicated by a cross.

Can you fill each square with the correct symbol?

Score

1					X X
2					X X
3					X X
4					X X
5					✓ X
6					✓ X
					✓✓✓✓

52

60 Spidoku

Each of the eight segments of the spider's web should be filled with a different number from 1 to 8, in such a way that every ring also contains a different number from 1 to 8.

The segments run from the outside of the spider's web to the centre, and the rings run all the way around.

Some numbers are already in place. Can you fill in the rest?

53

61 Wordfit

Fit the listed pond and lake plants and creatures into the grid below, then rearrange the letters in the shaded squares to form the name of something else you might see in a pond or lake.

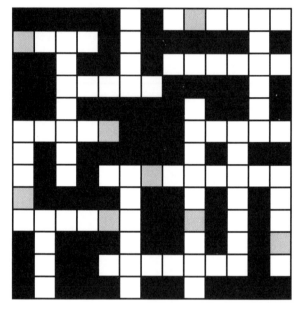

4 letters
CARP
PIKE
TOAD

5 letters
ALGAE
NEWTS
NYMPH
REEDS
ROCKS

6 letters
AMOEBA
LARVAE
MINNOW
RUSHES
STONES

7 letters
GRASSES
KINGCUP
PEBBLES

9 letters
DAMSEL FLY
FROGSPAWN

Birdsearch

Find the listed birds hidden in the grid below. Words run in either a forward or backward direction, horizontally, vertically or diagonally, but always in a straight line.

```
K S Q G K P V F L H E E Y
R C O W E A G L E B C H B
E H C N I F U O E H S R B
P I H A Y G R R O U D E O
E F G W L O G U R S O V H
E F L S B S G H U U E O P
R C N I G H T I N G A L E
C H N H N P W N B V O P M
E A G Z G N E E O R O O K
E F Z Y L V E C L H K K S
R F K P A L E T Z R C N F
T G H R U T L R U H U T D
O E R A F D L E I F C C F
```

AVOCET	FINCH	PLOVER
CHIFFCHAFF	GOOSE	RAVEN
CHOUGH	GREBE	ROBIN
CUCKOO	GULL	ROOK
CURLEW	HOBBY	SWAN
EAGLE	LINNET	THRUSH
FIELDFARE	NIGHTINGALE	TREECREEPER

Honeycomb

Place the letters of each word, one per cell, so that every word flows in a clockwise direction around a number.

Where the hexagons of one word overlap with those of another, the letter in each cell is common to both.

When finished, rearrange the letters in the pale green hexagons to form the name of a national park.

ACTIVE
COHORT
DEJECT
DEMURE

DEVOUR
LAWMEN
MAYHEM

ONRUSH
POLICE
TROPHY
VERNAL

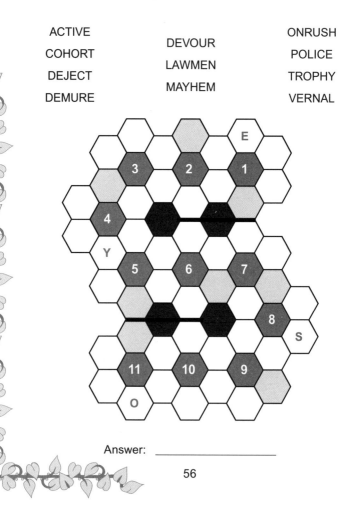

Answer: _____

64 Codeword

Every letter in this crossword has been replaced by a number, the number remaining the same for that letter wherever it occurs. Can you substitute numbers for letters and complete the crossword? One word has already been entered into the grid, to help you on your way.

When finished, use the code to spell out a sea creature.

A	9	17	22	18	21	20		25	6	22	7	7	8
B	18		17		18		20		16		13		11
C	1	17	18	8	2	20	10		4	13	22	23	20
D	20		20		22		10		20		6		22
E	12	14	10	20	24		6	9	13	18	1	11	2
F	10			16	20	24	18	22			11		11
G		3	12	6	17	20		14	22	17	2	15	
H	8		9			21	12	10	1	22			22
I	9 P	22	9	13	18	5	22		22	26	18	12	16
J	18 I		13		1		8		18		23		6
K	5 K	10	20	20	17		18	1	10	20	12	6	8
L	20 E		8		12		8		8		13		20
M	24	20	8	9	12	2		8	2	22	19	20	24

Letters down the right: N O P Q R S T U V W X Y Z

1	2	3	4	5 K	6	7	8	9 P	10	11	12	13
14	15	16	17	18 I	19	20 E	21	22	23	24	25	26

Answer

8	2	22	13	7	18	8	11

57

65 Wordladder

Change one letter at a time (but not the position of any letter) to make a new word – and move from the word at the top of the ladder to the word at the bottom using the exact number of rungs provided.

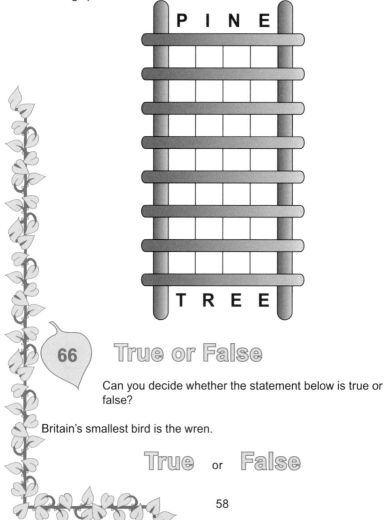

P I N E

T R E E

66 True or False

Can you decide whether the statement below is true or false?

Britain's smallest bird is the wren.

True or False

67 Petal Puzzle

How many words of three or more letters can you
make from those on the petals, without using plurals,
abbreviations or proper nouns? The central letter must appear once in
every word and no letter may be used more than once unless it is on
a different petal. There is at least one nine-letter word to be found.

68 Forested Areas

Fit the letters F, O, R, E, S and T into the grid in such a way that each horizontal row, each vertical column and each of the heavily outlined sections of six squares contains a different letter. Some letters are already in place.

E	F				
R			T	S	
O					

69 Insect Tracker

Starting at the top left corner and ending at the bottom right, track a path from letter to letter, in any direction except diagonally, in order to find the hidden insects and similar creatures. All of the letters must be used once only.

M	A	Y	F	P	E	L	O	U	S	I	P	L	A	C	E	W
N	O	G	L	I	D	E	A	E	E	R	H	T	E	D	N	I
F	L	A	Y	L	M	G	R	E	S	T	O	N	P	E	G	B
C	Y	R	D	L	I	I	W	L	L	A	Y	E	I	T	N	E
R	I	C	C	H	B	E	E	T	D	E	L	F	L	C	E	E
T	E	K	A	O	N	A	Y	L	F	R	R	I	I	A	I	T
C	O	C	K	R	T	F	L	E	A	S	P	N	G	T	C	K

60

Anagram Mountain

Correctly solve the anagrams each step of the way from the top to the bottom of the mountain and the name of a weather feature will be revealed in the central column of bricks.

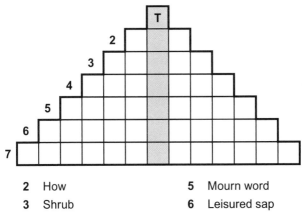

2	How	5	Mourn word
3	Shrub	6	Leisured sap
4	Lank bet	7	Pipe portrayal

71

Spelling Bee

Which is the only one of the following to be correctly spelled?

a CONVULVOLUS

b CONVOLVULUS

c CONVULVULUS

d CONVOLVOLUS

Natural Selection

Find the correct answer to each question from the four alternatives.

1 What is the name for a male pig?
  a. Bull
  b. Boar
  c. Hog
  d. Teg

2 What name is given to a full moon that occurs twice in the same month?
  a. Mock moon
  b. Hunter's moon
  c. Blue moon
  d. Harvest moon

3 What is the lowest point of the Kelvin temperature scale?
  a. Bottom zero
  b. One hundred
  c. Terminal zero
  d. Absolute zero

4 Which is the solar system's largest solid planet?
  a. Earth
  b. Venus
  c. Mars
  d. Jupiter

5 What kind of animal is a stonechat?
  a. Lizard
  b. Bird
  c. Snake
  d. Antelope

6 What is the world's tallest animal?
  a. Giraffe
  b. Okapi
  c. Saharan Camel
  d. Indian elephant

7 What kind of animal is a sarassa?
  a. Snake
  b. Seawater crocodile
  c. Fish
  d. Lizard

8 What kind of animal goes by the name of 'crown of thorns'?
  a. Porcupine
  b. Starfish
  c. Hedgehog
  d. Crab

73

Solve the crossword puzzle in the usual way, then rearrange the letters in the shaded squares to spell out a keyword: the name of a creature.

Across

3 Spectres (6)
6 Hollow metal device which rings when struck (4)
7 Particular example (8)
9 Foreman (4)
10 Located (8)
13 Without pips (8)
15 Arabian ruler (4)
16 By a circuitous route (8)
19 Adolescent (4)
20 Deported (6)

Down

1 Bring to an end, settle conclusively (7)
2 Ecstasy (5)
3 Nitrogen, for example (3)
4 Egg cells (3)
5 Rate of travel (5)
8 Bind (5)
11 Person who does no work (5)
12 In an aroused state (7)
13 Cut into pieces (5)
14 Fight (3-2)
17 Not in good health (3)
18 Come to a halt (3)

Whirlpool

74

Find a route for the fish to take in order to escape from the middle of the whirlpool to the calmer waters beyond.

75 Fruit Sudoku

Every row, every column and each of the nine smaller boxes of nine squares should be filled with a different number from 1 to 9 inclusive. Some numbers are already in place. When the grid is completely filled, decode the numbers in the shaded squares to spell out the name of a fruit. Every row should be read from left to right, starting from the top and working to the bottom of the grid.

	4		6		9			
8	5	3						
		2			3			
7					2	6		
	3			1			2	
		1	9					8
			2			7		
						3	8	2
			1		6		9	

Code

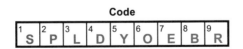

1	2	3	4	5	6	7	8	9
S	P	L	D	Y	O	E	B	R

Answer: _____

65

76 Shape-up

Every row and column in this grid originally contained one bird, one flower, one leaf, one mushroom and two blank squares, although not necessarily in that order. Every symbol with a black arrow refers to the first of the four symbols encountered in the direction of the arrow. Every symbol with a white arrow refers to the second of the four symbols encountered in the direction of the arrow. Can you complete the original grid?

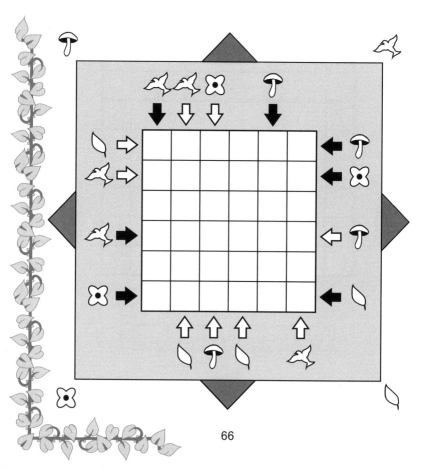

Round Dozen

First solve the clues. All of the solutions end with the letter in the middle of the circle, and in every word an additional letter is in place. When the puzzle is complete, you can then go on to discover two trees, reading clockwise around the green ring of letters.

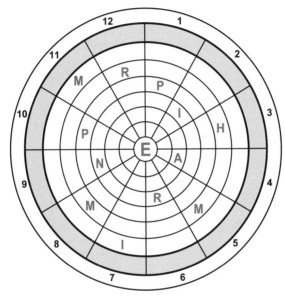

1 Precious blue gemstone

2 Tiny piece of anything

3 Practise

4 Final

5 White-flowered plant used medicinally

6 Leave one's country of residence for a new one

7 Trachea

8 Not fully developed

9 Popular soft drink

10 Ambiguity in the law or a contract

11 Eater of meat and vegetables

12 Clothes closet

Answer: _____ and _____

Natural Selection

Find the correct answer to each question from the four alternatives.

1 Which main feature distinguishes hares from rabbits?
a. The ears   **b.** The tail
c. The lips   **d.** The colour of the eyes

2 To which family of birds does the crossbill belong?
a. Parrot   **b.** Crow
c. Finch   **d.** Hawk

3 What is the male counterpart of the honey-bee?
a. Queen   **b.** Worker
c. Bumble   **d.** Drone

4 How many eyes do the majority of species of spider have?
a. Eight   **b.** Six
c. Four   **d.** Sixteen

5 Which creature is the emblem of India, Malaysia and South Korea?
a. Panda   **b.** Elephant
c. Tiger   **d.** Eagle

6 Which of these four is the oldest breed of dog?
a. Chow chow   **b.** Dachshund
c. Corgi   **d.** Greyhound

7 Where do arboreal animals make their homes?
a. In caves   **b.** In trees
c. In the ground   **d.** On the ground

8 What Spanish-derived name is given to the droppings of birds?
a. Guacamole   **b.** Guano
c. Guaco   **d.** Guaramo

Pine Forest

The object of this puzzle is to trace a single path from the top left square to the bottom right square of the grid, moving through all of the cells in either a horizontal, vertical or diagonal direction. Every cell must be entered once only and your path should take you through the letters in the sequence P-I-N-E-P-I-N-E, etc. Can you find the logical way through?

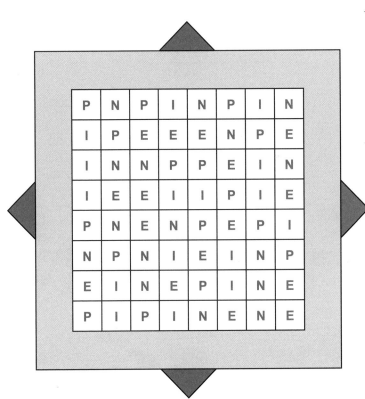

P	N	P	I	N	P	I	N
I	P	E	E	E	N	P	E
I	N	N	P	P	E	I	N
I	E	E	I	I	P	I	E
P	N	E	N	P	E	P	I
N	P	N	I	E	I	N	P
E	I	N	E	P	I	N	E
P	I	P	I	N	E	N	E

80 **What's It Worth?**

Each symbol stands for a different number. In order to reach the correct total at the end of each row and column, what is the value of the bat, frog, rabbit and starfish?

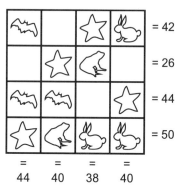

				= 42
				= 26
				= 44
				= 50

=44 =40 =38 =40

81 **Shape Spotter**

Which is the only shape to appear twice in exactly the same shading (black, white or green) in the box below? You'll need a keen eye for this one, as some shapes overlap others!

70

82 Riddle-Me-Ree

Find one letter per line, following the clues given in the verse below. For example, 'My first is in houses, but never in homes' gives the letter U as the first letter. When you have finished, the letters will spell another word.

My first is in BRUSH, but never in BROOM,

My second's in BRIDE, but not found in GROOM,

My third is in ADULT, and also in CHILD,

My fourth is in GENTLE, but not seen in MILD,

My fifth's not in SWORD, though it is found in SHIELD,

My whole is a boundary, ringing a field.

1st	2nd	3rd	4th	5th

83 True or False

Can you decide whether the statement below is true or false?

After eating aphids, the lacewing uses the skins for camouflage against insect-eating birds.

True or False

84 Telephone Code

Use the telephone dial in order to spell out a quotation attributed to Rebecca West.

2 4 2   8 1 4 6 8   3 7 1 6 2 4 8   6 7 3 1 2 4   8 6

8 4 3   1 4 7 2 8 ?   9 4 1 8 3 9 3 7   3 6 7 ?

4 3   4 3   7 3 1 5 5 0   5 4 4 3 2   1 4 7 2 8   4 3

9 6 9 5 2   4 1 9 3   2 6 6 3   1 3 8 8 3 7   8 6

6 7 3 1 2 4   8 6   8 4 3   2 1 8 8 .

72

NNR Arroword

Place the answers in the direction shown by the arrows for each clue. When finished, the letters in the green squares can be rearranged to spell out the name of a National Nature Reserve in Shropshire.

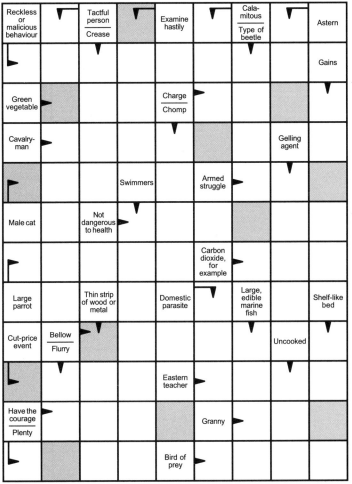

Mix 'n' Match

Pair up each of the boxes below to form the names of eight different fungi.

BALL

HER

FLE

ETUS

BLE

PUFF

ETTE

GRIS

DECE

IVER

BOL

BLUS

DER

TRUF

TIN

WIT

Round the Block

You won't need a starting block to get you under way, because it isn't a race! Just arrange the six-letter solutions to the clues into the six blocks around each clue number. Write the answers in a clockwise or anticlockwise direction and you'll find that the last answer fits into the first; the main problem will be to decide in which square to put the first letter of each word…

When read in a clockwise direction (not necessarily starting at either of the topmost squares), the letters in the pale green squares spell out the name of a part of a plant.

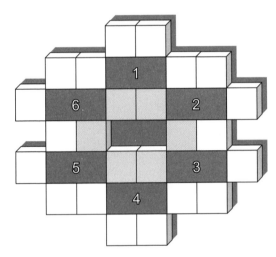

1 Common root vegetable

2 Law enforcement agency

3 More sacred

4 Not deceptive or fraudulent

5 Bundle of fibres running to various organs and tissues of the body

6 Paper fastener made of wire

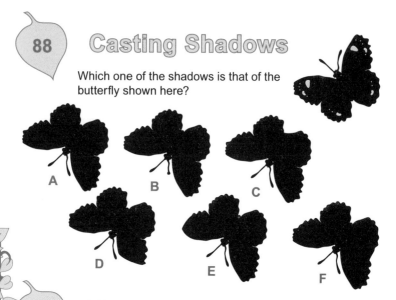

88 Casting Shadows

Which one of the shadows is that of the butterfly shown here?

A

B

C

D

E

F

89 The Bottom Line

The bottom line of this grid is waiting to be filled. Every square in the solution contains only one symbol from rows 1 to 5 above, although two or more squares in the solution may contain the same symbol. At the end of every numbered row is a score, which shows:

1. the number of symbols placed in the correct finishing position on the bottom line, as indicated by a tick; and

2. the number of symbols which appear on the bottom line, but in a different position, as indicated by a cross.

Can you fill each square with the correct symbol?

					Score
1	🕷	🦢	🦇	🍄	X X
2	🦋	🪰	🍄	🦭	X X
3	🍄	🕷	🦇	🦇	X X
4	🪰	🍃	🦭	🦢	X
5	🦇	🍄	🕷	🦭	✓✓
					✓✓✓✓

76

90 Spidoku

Each of the eight segments of the spider's web should be filled with a different number from 1 to 8, in such a way that every ring also contains a different number from 1 to 8.

The segments run from the outside of the spider's web to the centre, and the rings run all the way around.

Some numbers are already in place. Can you fill in the rest?

91 Wordfit

Fit the listed items of hiking gear into the grid below, then rearrange the letters in the shaded squares to form the name of another item useful when hiking.

3 letters
HAT
MAP

4 letters
FOOD

5 letters
BOOTS
KNIFE
SCARF
SOCKS
TORCH

6 letters
CAMERA
GLOVES

7 letters
COMPASS
MATCHES

10 letters
BINOCULARS
FIELD GUIDE

11 letters
FIRST-AID KIT
MOBILE PHONE

78

Picnic Wordsearch

Find the listed picnic words hidden in the grid below.
Words run in either a forward or backward direction,
horizontally, vertically or diagonally, but always in a straight line.

```
S T Q E L P P A S S Z U B
N L Q Y S H U T K S U C C
U O L O T E I R Q Q C S O
B P S O E U O W E N H E U
Q E L R R F O T S M Q R P
O C B F E M T L A P S V S
T R B B A K A L L M N I E
K E A A K W C H A Q O E V
S T H N B I I A D S O T I
A A L A G N B C R B P T N
L W V N E E F F O C S E K
F L I A K X L W X A K S D
H L H U S E L K C I P H G
```

APPLE	FLASK	SALAD
BANANA	FORKS	SALT
BOWL	FRUIT	SERVIETTES
BUNS	HAM ROLLS	SPOONS
CLOTH	KNIVES	TOMATOES
COFFEE	ORANGE	WATER
CRACKERS	PICKLES	WINE

93 Honeycomb

Place the letters of each word, one per cell, so that every word flows in a clockwise direction around a number.

Where the hexagons of one word overlap with those of another, the letter in each cell is common to both.

When finished, rearrange the letters in the pale green hexagons to form the name of a range of hills.

BICEPS

CHEESE

NOODLE

PELVIS

PYRITE

SEXTET

SPOOKY

TRAVEL

TUMBLE

VAGARY

VOTIVE

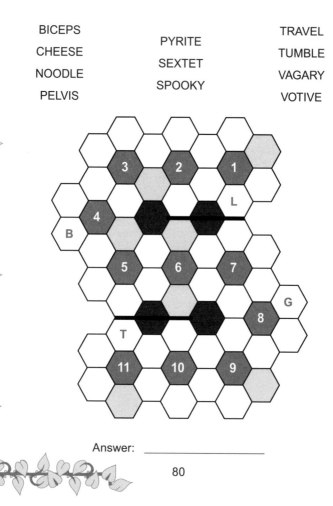

Answer: _____

94 Codeword

Every letter in this crossword has been replaced by a number, the number remaining the same for that letter wherever it occurs. Can you substitute numbers for letters and complete the crossword? One word has already been entered into the grid, to help you on your way.
When finished, use the code to spell out a type of beetle.

A	4	15	5	24	13 B	12	22	10	16		18	10	9	N
B	22		8		10 I		13		26		7		22	O
C	13	16	5	12	18 D	7	25		16	10	24	10	4	P
D			16		7 E		26		16		26		7	Q
E	22	21	22	25		13	22	12	10	3	4	7	25	R
F	8				24		18		9		7		12	S
G	22	12	17	15	26	25		13	26	12	3	22	10	T
H	16		22		3		20		9				4	U
I	22	12	4	10	14	5	7	3		1	22	23	6	V
J	12		7		5		12		19		16			W
K	17	26	25	11	10		10	24	22	11	10	12	7	X
L	15		7		4		4		10		13		2	Y
M	7	22	25		26	4	15	7	25	1	10	3	7	Z

1	2	3	4	5	6	7	8	9	10	11	12	13
						E			I			B
14	**15**	**16**	**17**	**18**	**19**	**20**	**21**	**22**	**23**	**24**	**25**	**26**
				D								

Answer

16	22	18	6	13	10	25	18

95 Wordladder

Change one letter at a time (but not the position of any letter) to make a new word – and move from the word at the top of the ladder to the word at the bottom using the exact number of rungs provided.

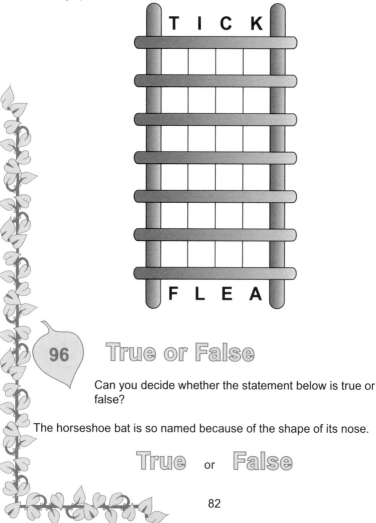

T I C K

F L E A

96 True or False

Can you decide whether the statement below is true or false?

The horseshoe bat is so named because of the shape of its nose.

True or False

82

Petal Puzzle

How many words of three or more letters can you make from those on the petals, without using plurals, abbreviations or proper nouns? The central letter must appear once in every word and no letter may be used more than once unless it is on a different petal. There is at least one nine-letter word to be found.

_____

_____

_____

_____

_____

_____

_____

98 Forested Areas

Fit the letters F, O, R, E, S and T into the grid in such a way that each horizontal row, each vertical column and each of the heavily outlined sections of six squares contains a different letter. Some letters are already in place.

S		E		F	
	T				
				R	
	O				

99 Mineral Tracker

Starting at the top left corner and ending at the bottom right, track a path from letter to letter, in any direction except diagonally, in order to find the hidden rocks, stones and minerals. All of the letters must be used once only.

F	L	U	O	R	A	R	I	T	A	R	B	E	S	A	N	D
T	S	Y	H	I	B	U	Q	E	M	E	L	N	O	O	T	S
C	A	L	T	T	E	A	A	T	E	S	E	S	T	N	E	G
T	I	C	E	M	A	R	G	E	L	E	M	I	L	R	E	R
E	A	M	T	J	Z	T	A	N	I	T	E	J	A	S	P	A
R	E	B	E	E	E	R	E	N	I	I	L	F	E	T	I	N
G	A	R	N	T	S	P	E	N	T	N	T	S	L	A	T	E

Anagram Mountain

Correctly solve the anagrams each step of the way from the top to the bottom of the mountain and the name of a plant or animal will be revealed in the central column of bricks.

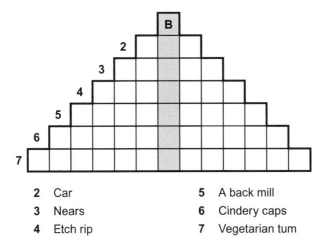

2	Car	5	A back mill
3	Nears	6	Cindery caps
4	Etch rip	7	Vegetarian tum

101

Spelling Bee

Which is the only one of the following to be correctly spelled?

a   FUMITORY

b   FUMETORY

c   FUMETARY

d   FUMITARY

Find the correct answer to each question from the four alternatives.

1 What term is applied to describe cud-chewing mammals?
  a. Carnivore   **b.** Herbivore
  c. Ruminant   **d.** Ungulate

2 Which order makes up the largest proportion of mammals?
  a. Rodents   **b.** Primates
  c. Carnivores   **d.** Cetaceans

3 Where in Europe do apes live out of captivity?
  a. Corsica   **b.** Sardinia
  c. Gibraltar   **d.** Sicily

4 Rats are unable to do which bodily function, making them more vulnerable to poisoning?
  a. Cough   **b.** Urinate
  c. Sneeze   **d.** Vomit

5 What is missing from a navel orange?
  a. Pith   **b.** Pips
  c. Stalk   **d.** Segments

6 What is the only insect to be completely domesticated in order to be specifically useful to man?
  a. Bee   **b.** Caterpillar
  c. Ant   **d.** Silkworm

7 What do animals shed when they desquamate?
  a. Skin   **b.** Hair
  c. Horn   **d.** Tail

8 What is the world's most widely cultivated foodstuff?
  a. Maize   **b.** Potato
  c. Wheat   **d.** Rice

Solve the crossword puzzle in the usual way, then rearrange the letters in the shaded squares to spell out a keyword: the name of a creature.

Across

3 Separate into parts (5,2)
7 Beaver-like animal (5)
8 Substitute (7)
9 Ocean-going vessel (5)
10 Perpetual (7)
12 More than is needed (7)
16 Country, capital Beijing (5)
17 Diffusing warmth and friendliness (7)
19 Daughter of a sibling (5)
20 Number in one century (7)

Down

1 Burn with steam (5)
2 Passing from physical life (5)
3 Resembling a dream (7)
4 Cut back the growth of (3)
5 Banter (5)
6 Machine used for printing (5)
11 Move downward and lower (7)
12 Pulverise (5)
13 Have sovereign power (5)
14 Donated (5)
15 Desert animal (5)
18 Rigid piece of metal (3)

Whirlpool

Find a route for the fish to take in order to escape from the middle of the whirlpool to the calmer waters beyond.

105 Plant Sudoku

Every row, every column and each of the nine smaller boxes of nine squares should be filled with a different number from 1 to 9 inclusive. Some numbers are already in place. When the grid is completely filled, decode the numbers in the shaded squares to spell out the name of a plant. Every row should be read from left to right, starting from the top and working to the bottom of the grid.

		2			7	9	5	
			5				4	
1	5			6				
	9	5	7	3		4		
2								9
		6		1	9	5	2	
				7			9	4
	7				1			
	6	1	8			3		

Code

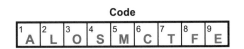

1	2	3	4	5	6	7	8	9
A	L	O	S	M	C	T	F	E

Answer: _____

Every row and column in this grid originally contained one bird, one flower, one leaf, one mushroom and two blank squares, although not necessarily in that order. Every symbol with a black arrow refers to the first of the four symbols encountered in the direction of the arrow. Every symbol with a white arrow refers to the second of the four symbols encountered in the direction of the arrow. Can you complete the original grid?

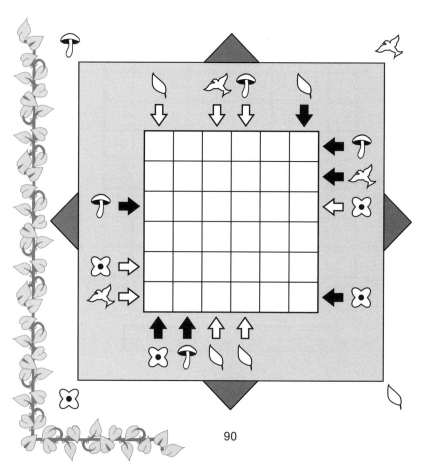

107 Round Dozen

First solve the clues. All of the solutions end with the letter in the middle of the circle, and in every word an additional letter is in place. When the puzzle is complete, you can then go on to discover a bird, reading clockwise around the green ring of letters.

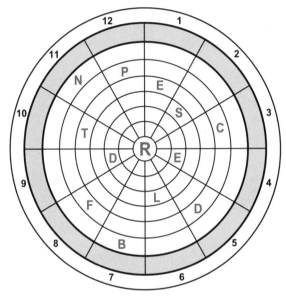

1	List of dates	**7**	Slaughterhouse
2	Family member from the remote past	**8**	Substandard
		9	Aromatic shrub
3	Queer	**10**	College tutor
4	Designer of machinery	**11**	Of the middle of a region or country
5	Heating appliance		
6	Royalist supporter of Charles I	**12**	Adventurer

Answer: _____

91

Natural Selection

Find the correct answer to each question from the four alternatives.

1 What is the name for a beaver's home?
    a. Sett   **b.** Dray
    c. House   **d.** Lodge

2 Native to southern Africa, what kind of bird is an aasvogel?
    a. Vulture   **b.** Goose
    c. Duck   **d.** Swan

3 A mahout looks after and drives which kind of animal?
    a. Horse   **b.** Camel
    c. Elephant   **d.** Cow

4 What colour is the tongue of a chow?
    a. Yellow   **b.** Blue-black
    c. Orange-pink   **d.** Brown

5 Which is the only mammal with four forward-bending knees?
    a. Llama   **b.** Camel
    c. Caribou   **d.** Elephant

6 Mohair wool is obtained from which species of goat?
    a. Astrakhan   **b.** Angora
    c. Cashmere   **d.** Russian white

7 Foehns, chinooks and mistrals are types of what?
    a. Clouds   **b.** Winds
    c. Deer   **d.** Horses

8 What is the main ingredient of sauerkraut?
    a. Beetroot   **b.** Cauliflower
    c. Cucumber/gherkins   **d.** Cabbage

Pine Forest

The object of this puzzle is to trace a single path from the top left square to the bottom right square of the grid, moving through all of the cells in either a horizontal, vertical or diagonal direction. Every cell must be entered once only and your path should take you through the letters in the sequence P-I-N-E-P-I-N-E, etc. Can you find the logical way through?

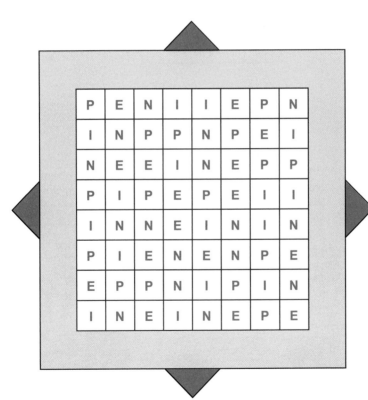

P	E	N	I	I	E	P	N
I	N	P	P	N	P	E	I
N	E	E	I	N	E	P	P
P	I	P	E	P	E	I	I
I	N	N	E	I	N	I	N
P	I	E	N	E	N	P	E
E	P	P	N	I	P	I	N
I	N	E	I	N	E	P	E

110 What's It Worth?

Each symbol stands for a different number. In order to reach the correct total at the end of each row and column, what is the value of the bat, frog, rabbit and starfish?

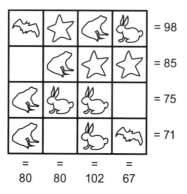

111 Shape Spotter

Which is the only shape to appear twice in exactly the same shading (black, white or green) in the box below? You'll need a keen eye for this one, as some shapes overlap others!

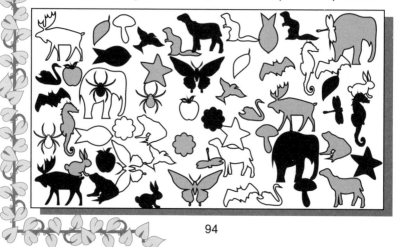

94

112 Riddle-Me-Ree

Find one letter per line, following the clues given in the verse below. For example, 'My first is in houses, but never in homes' gives the letter U as the first letter. When you have finished, the letters will spell another word.

My first's not in RIVER, but is found in STREAM,

My second's in REVERIE, never in DREAM,

My third is in TOAD, but not seen in FROG,

My fourth is in DRAGON, and also in DOG,

My fifth is in NOSE, and also in EYE,

My whole is a troublesome, small biting fly.

1st	2nd	3rd	4th	5th

113 True or False

Can you decide whether the statement below is true or false?

The Galápagos fur seal is the largest of all the fur seals.

True or **False**

Telephone Code

Use the telephone dial in order to spell out a quotation attributed to John Berger.

6 6 8 4 4 6 3 4 6 8 4 3 6 1 8 9 7 2 1 7 6 9 6 2 9 8 4 8

3 9 4 5 . 8 4 4 8 6 3 3 2 8 8 6 1 3 7 3 6 3 1 8 3 2 8 4 6 2 3

6 6 3 6 3 8 4 3 4 9 5 1 6 9 1 0 8 6 3 8 1 5 4 4 6 3

6 6 3 8 3 5 3 4 6 8 6 4 6 4 9 5 1 6 1 2 8 8 4 8 8 6 2 4 8 3

8 4 3 8 9 6 6 6 8 3 2 2 7 9 3 5 8 0 6 3 6 1 8 9 7 3 .

Place the answers in the direction shown by the arrows for each clue. When finished, the letters in the green squares can be rearranged to spell out the name of a National Nature Reserve in Essex.

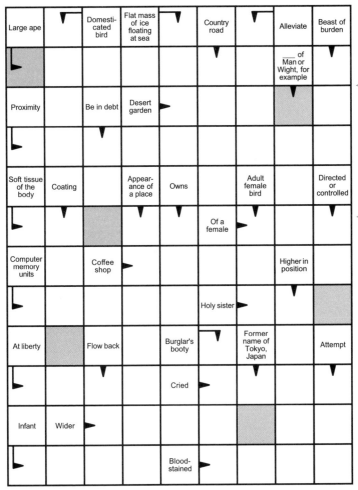

Mix 'n' Match

116

Pair up each of the boxes below to form the names of eight different birds.

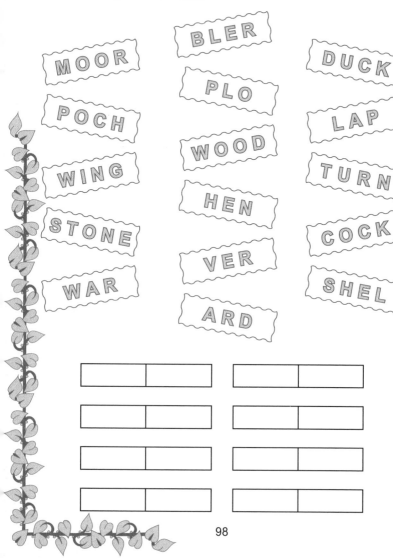

MOOR
BLER
DUCK
POCH
PLO
LAP
WING
WOOD
TURN
STONE
HEN
COCK
WAR
VER
SHEL
ARD

98

Round the Block

You won't need a starting block to get you under way, because it isn't a race! Just arrange the six-letter solutions to the clues into the six blocks around each clue number. Write the answers in a clockwise or anticlockwise direction and you'll find that the last answer fits into the first; the main problem will be to decide in which square to put the first letter of each word…

When read in a clockwise direction (not necessarily starting at either of the topmost squares), the letters in the pale green squares spell out the name of a tree or shrub.

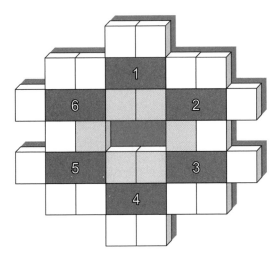

1 Substance used in making soap, candles and lubricants

2 Beast, creature

3 Large herbivorous arboreal lizard of tropical America

4 Economical, avoiding waste

5 Gallic

6 Taken without permission

Casting Shadows

Which one of the shadows is that of the heron shown here?

A

B

C

D

E

F

The Bottom Line

The bottom line of this grid is waiting to be filled. Every square in the solution contains only one symbol from rows 1 to 5 above, although two or more squares in the solution may contain the same symbol. At the end of every numbered row is a score, which shows:

1 the number of symbols placed in the correct finishing position on the bottom line, as indicated by a tick; and

2 the number of symbols which appear on the bottom line, but in a different position, as indicated by a cross.

Can you fill each square with the correct symbol?

				Score
1				X X
2				✓
3				✓
4				✓
5				X X
				✓✓✓✓

100

Spidoku

Each of the eight segments of the spider's web should be filled with a different number from 1 to 8, in such a way that every ring also contains a different number from 1 to 8. The segments run from the outside of the spider's web to the centre, and the rings run all the way around.
Some numbers are already in place. Can you fill in the rest?

101

Wordfit

Fit the listed deserts into the grid below, then rearrange the letters in the shaded squares to form the name of another desert.

4 letters
GOBI
THAR

5 letters
KAVIR
MONTE
NAMIB
NEGEV
ORDOS

6 letters
ACCONA
GIBSON
TANAMI

7 letters
AL-DAHNA
ARABIAN
ATACAMA
SIMPSON
SONORAN

8 letters
TABERNAS

10 letters
STRZELECKI

11 letters
GREAT INDIAN

Farming Wordsearch

Find the listed farming words hidden in the grid below.
Words run in either a forward or backward direction,
horizontally, vertically or diagonally, but always in a straight line.

```
S W K R O T A V I T L U C
P T Q B W F J A S P M H P
E O I O U Y J N Y R I A D
E P F U G L R C T C C O X
H I R O R A L X K R N J H
S G O O B F Q E E K L E E
K S R D T J N A E U C G H
E I I A G C G Y A T K J E
M L C C I E A K A R S C I
K O H Y K N A R C U N C F
H T G O O L E Y T E O N E
E H T Y C S E C F R U N R
C R E L I A R T N Y H O D
```

ACREAGE	DONKEY	PIGS
BARNS	FENCE	SCYTHE
BULL	FRUIT	SHEEP
CHICKEN	GOOSE	SICKLE
CORN	GRAIN	SILO
CULTIVATOR	HECTARES	TRACTOR
DAIRY	HEIFER	TRAILER

Honeycomb

Place the letters of each word, one per cell, so that every word flows in a clockwise direction around a number.

Where the hexagons of one word overlap with those of another, the letter in each cell is common to both.

When finished, rearrange the letters in the pale green hexagons to form the name of a season.

BRAINY

BREECH

COLUMN

HEREBY

MARTYR

MILDEW

OPTIMA

POSTAL

SOCKET

SULTRY

TRANCE

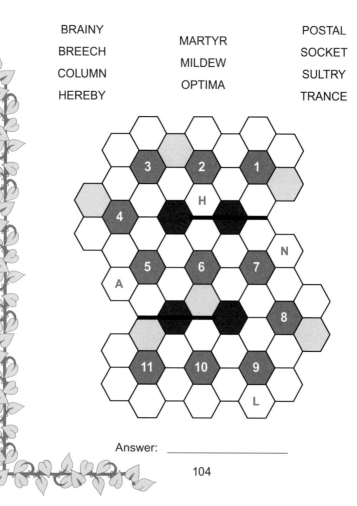

Answer: _____

Every letter in this crossword has been replaced by a number, the number remaining the same for that letter wherever it occurs. Can you substitute numbers for letters and complete the crossword? One word has already been entered into the grid, to help you on your way.

When finished, use the code to spell out a plant.

A	2	20	26	3		26 **A**	17	18	26	16	9	14	13
B		25		9		3 **M**		9		8			23
C	26	14	26	13	21	9 **E**	3	26		26	7	8	9
D		16		9		14 **N**		8		3			26
E	4	9	7	23	26		19	11	3	19	11	24	2
F			24			2		24			8		11
G	18	24	22	13	26	19	11	2	25	13	25	11	14
H	24		11			9		15			12		
I	1	25	3	3	25	16	10		17	23	9	26	3
J	24			26		25		6		11		8	
K	8	24	14	1		5	11	24	14	13	26	25	14
L	26			3		25		26		11		9	
M	23	11	3	26	14	16	9	17		23	9	14	13

Letters down the right side: N O P Q R S T U V W X Y Z

1	2	3 **M**	4	5	6	7	8	9 **E**	10	11	12	13
14 **N**	15	16	17	18	19	20	21	22	23	24	25	26 **A**

Answer

19	9	23	25	20	25	14	10	8	9

105

125 Wordladder

Change one letter at a time (but not the position of any letter) to make a new word – and move from the word at the top of the ladder to the word at the bottom using the exact number of rungs provided.

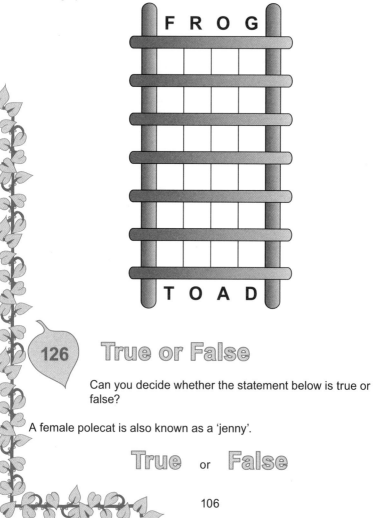

F R O G

T O A D

126 True or False

Can you decide whether the statement below is true or false?

A female polecat is also known as a 'jenny'.

True or False

Petal Puzzle

How many words of three or more letters can you make from those on the petals, without using plurals, abbreviations or proper nouns? The central letter must appear once in every word and no letter may be used more than once unless it is on a different petal. There is at least one nine-letter word to be found.

128

Fit the letters F, O, R, E, S and T into the grid in such a way that each horizontal row, each vertical column and each of the heavily outlined sections of six squares contains a different letter. Some letters are already in place.

	E				F
			S		
T					
		R			
	O				

129 Rural Skills Tracker

Starting at the top left corner and ending at the bottom right, track a path from letter to letter, in any direction except diagonally, in order to find the hidden rural skills, occupations and trades. All of the letters must be used once only.

F	M	A	A	R	R	G	E	K	E	E	P	E	R	F	A	R
A	H	N	C	T	E	A	M	M	N	A	E	V	I	A	E	M
R	G	U	O	L	S	E	R	I	L	M	R	A	D	M	R	M
R	I	E	R	P	T	E	O	F	L	R	W	E	F	K	L	I
A	D	D	R	E	H	R	S	R	E	E	H	S	I	H	A	T
I	M	A	W	I	P	E	H	D	W	E	L	I	G	T	H	C
R	Y	N	S	N	E	H	E	R	H	E	W	R	H	T	E	R

Anagram Mountain

Correctly solve the anagrams each step of the way from the top to the bottom of the mountain and the name of a weather feature will be revealed in the central column of bricks.

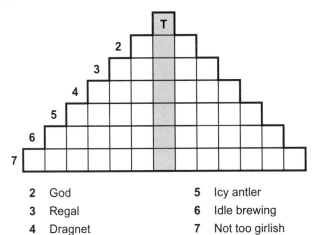

2	God	5	Icy antler
3	Regal	6	Idle brewing
4	Dragnet	7	Not too girlish

131

Spelling Bee

Which is the only one of the following to be correctly spelled?

a HELIBORE

b HELLEBORE

c HELLIBORE

d HELLABORE

Natural Selection

Find the correct answer to each question from the four alternatives.

1 Which of the following has blue flowers?
   a. Betony   **b.** Bistort
   c. Brooklime   **d.** Butterbur

2 Herb Robert has a pink flower, with how many petals?
   a. Three   **b.** Four
   c. Five   **d.** Six

3 Lesser Black-backed and Great Black-backed are types of which seabird?
   a. Tern   **b.** Gull
   c. Auk   **d.** Fulmar

4 Atlas, Cyprus, Lebanon and Deodar are all types of which tree?
   a. Pine   **b.** Cypress
   c. Oak   **d.** Cedar

5 What colour are the petals of woad flowers?
   a. Yellow   **b.** Purple
   c. White   **d.** Blue

6 What is the common name for the tree *Pinus pinaster*?
   a. Scots pine   **b.** Austrian pine
   c. Corsican pine   **d.** Maritime pine

7 What is the collective name for a group of wild geese in flight?
   a. Gaggle   **b.** Flock
   c. Skein   **d.** Chevron

8 To which genus of plants does the Meadow Cranesbill belong?
   a. Geranium   **b.** Narcissus
   c. Anemone   **d.** Acis

Keyword Crossword

Solve the crossword puzzle in the usual way, then rearrange the letters in the shaded squares to spell out a keyword: the name of a creature.

Across

1 Abnormally fat (5)
4 Pointed (5)
7 Military trainee (5)
8 Pandemonium (5)
9 Usually (2,1,4)
12 Organ of sight (3)
13 Clinging plant (3)
14 Arid regions of the world (7)
17 Roused from slumber (5)
18 Largest artery of the body (5)
19 Bottomless gulf or pit (5)
20 Precious stone (5)

Down

2 Section of an orchestra (5)
3 Utter obscenities (5)
4 Victory (7)
5 Lacking professional skill (7)
6 Own (7)
9 Fictional character in the *Arabian Nights* (3,4)
10 No-one in particular (7)
11 Disrobe (7)
15 Conjure up in the memory (5)
16 Identifying appellation (5)

Whirlpool

Find a route for the fish to take in order to escape from the middle of the whirlpool to the calmer waters beyond.

Geographical Sudoku

Every row, every column and each of the nine smaller boxes of nine squares should be filled with a different number from 1 to 9 inclusive. Some numbers are already in place. When the grid is completely filled, decode the numbers in the shaded squares to spell out the name of a range of hills. Every row should be read from left to right, starting from the top and working to the bottom of the grid.

	9			8	4			
8		7	9			5		
						2		
4		8	2	9			7	
	2			5			1	
	5			4	6	3		2
		4						
		2			8	9		1
			5	6			3	

Code

1	2	3	4	5	6	7	8	9
V	E	I	P	C	H	S	T	O

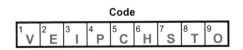

Answer: _____

136 Shape-up

Every row and column in this grid originally contained one bird, one flower, one leaf, one mushroom and two blank squares, although not necessarily in that order. Every symbol with a black arrow refers to the first of the four symbols encountered in the direction of the arrow. Every symbol with a white arrow refers to the second of the four symbols encountered in the direction of the arrow. Can you complete the original grid?

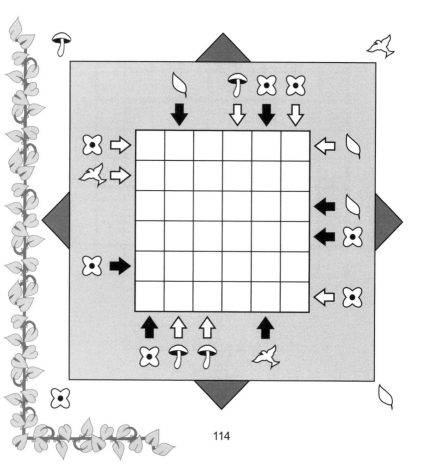

Round Dozen

First solve the clues. All of the solutions end with the letter in the middle of the circle, and in every word an additional letter is in place. When the puzzle is complete, you can then go on to discover a bird, reading clockwise around the green ring of letters.

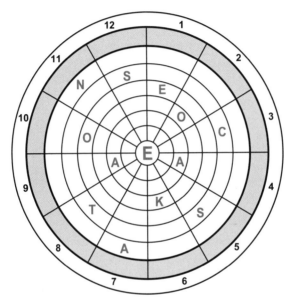

1 National Park in California, famed for its waterfalls

2 Worker

3 Ballgame played with long-handled racquets

4 Rise in the air and float, as if in defiance of gravity

5 Barrier

6 Debris

7 Components making up a computer system

8 Trigger off

9 Wedding

10 Learn by heart

11 Container for a letter, thin package, etc

12 Vibrate with sound

Answer: _____

Natural Selection

Find the correct answer to each question from the four alternatives.

1 What colour are the petals of the Common houndstongue?
   a. Blue   **b.** Red
   c. White   **d.** Yellow

2 Which common plant is known as the Butterfly bush?
   a. Gorse   **b.** Rhododendron
   c. Ivy   **d.** Buddleia

3 Bird, Wild and Sour are all types of which tree?
   a. Cherry   **b.** Plum
   c. Hawthorn   **d.** Poplar

4 Which tree of the poplar genus is easily identified by its leaves, that rustle in the lightest wind, hence its name *Populus tremula*?
   a. Black poplar   **b.** Abele
   c. Aspen   **d.** Grey poplar

5 Which native British bird has Grey, White, and Pied varieties?
   a. Heron   **b.** Pigeon
   c. Wagtail   **d.** Plover

6 *Fraxinus excelsior* is the Latin name of which tree?
   a. Common ash   **b.** Mountain ash
   c. Pallis ash   **d.** Flowering ash

7 What is the more prosaic name for Scorpion grass?
   a. Wild strawberry   **b.** Forget-me-not
   c. Ground elder   **d.** Hogweed

8 Which is NOT an alternative name for Cow parsley?
   a. Lady's lace   **b.** Rabbit's meat
   c. Keck   **d.** Robin's foot

139　Pine Forest

The object of this puzzle is to trace a single path from the top left square to the bottom right square of the grid, moving through all of the cells in either a horizontal, vertical or diagonal direction. Every cell must be entered once only and your path should take you through the letters in the sequence P-I-N-E-P-I-N-E, etc. Can you find the logical way through?

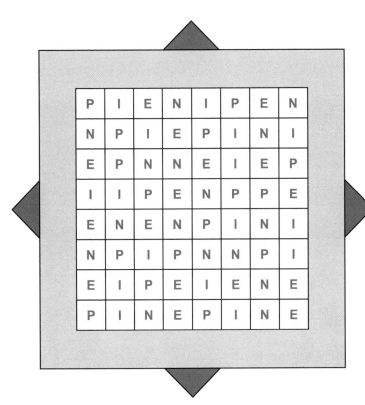

P	I	E	N	I	P	E	N
N	P	I	E	P	I	N	I
E	P	N	N	E	I	E	P
I	I	P	E	N	P	P	E
E	N	E	N	P	I	N	I
N	P	I	P	N	N	P	I
E	I	P	E	I	E	N	E
P	I	N	E	P	I	N	E

140 What's It Worth?

Each symbol stands for a different number. In order to reach the correct total at the end of each row and column, what is the value of the bat, frog, rabbit and starfish?

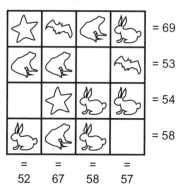

star	bat	frog	rabbit	= 69
frog	frog		bat	= 53
	star	rabbit	rabbit	= 54
rabbit	frog	rabbit		= 58
= 52	= 67	= 58	= 57	

141 Shape Spotter

Which is the only shape to appear twice in exactly the same shading (black, white or green) in the box below? You'll need a keen eye for this one, as some shapes overlap others!

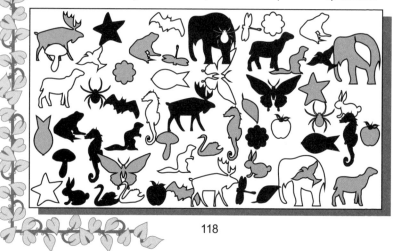

118

142 Riddle-Me-Ree

Find one letter per line, following the clues given in the verse below. For example, 'My first is in houses, but never in homes' gives the letter U as the first letter. When you have finished, the letters will spell another word.

My first is in ROUND, but never in SQUARE,

My second's in RABBIT, but never in HARE,

My third's not in CHICKEN, but is seen in HATCH,

My fourth's not in STRIKE, but it is found in MATCH,

My fifth's not in STRAW, but it is found in HAY,

My whole has been dug to drain water away.

1st	2nd	3rd	4th	5th

143 True or False

Can you decide whether the statement below is true or false?

A giraffe's jaw has no upper incisors, only lower incisors that are used to grasp leaves by trapping them against the hard palate.

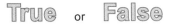

True or False

119

Telephone Code

Use the telephone dial in order to spell out a quotation attributed to Orison Swett Marden.

3 6 7 3 8 8 8 , 5 1 4 3 8 , 1 6 2 7 4 9 3 7 8 , 2 5 6 9 2 8 1 6 2

9 4 6 2 8 , 8 8 1 7 8 1 6 2 3 5 6 9 3 7 8 , 8 8 9 6 3 6 2 6 9 8

3 5 1 2 4 3 7 8 1 6 2 2 7 0 8 8 1 5 8 6 6 9 3 5 1 4 3 8 – 3 9 3 7 0

3 6 7 5 6 3 1 6 4 5 1 8 3 6 7 4 6 1 6 4 5 1 8 3 3 0 4 8 8 3 6 2 3 ,

5 3 1 9 3 8 4 8 8 4 5 6 7 3 8 8 9 6 6 6 8 4 3 8 6 9 5 6 3 5 1 6 .

NNR Arroword

Place the answers in the direction shown by the arrows for each clue. When finished, the letters in the green squares can be rearranged to spell out the name of a National Nature Reserve in County Down.

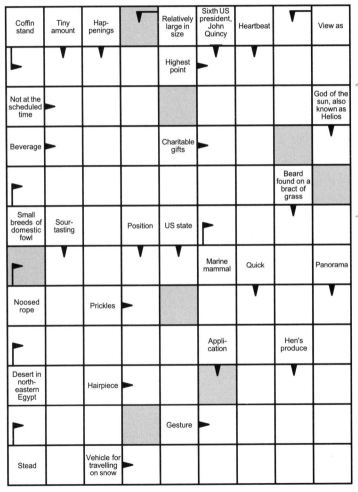

Coffin stand	Tiny amount	Hap-penings	▼	Relatively large in size	Sixth US president, John Quincy	Heartbeat	▼	View as
⌐	▼	▼		Highest point	▼	▼		
Not at the scheduled time ►								God of the sun, also known as Helios
Beverage ►				Charitable gifts ►				▼
⌐							Beard found on a bract of grass	
Small breeds of domestic fowl	Sour-tasting		Position	US state	►		▼	
⌐	▼		▼	▼	Marine mammal	Quick		Panorama
Noosed rope		Prickles ►				▼		▼
⌐				Appli-cation		Hen's produce		
Desert in north-eastern Egypt		Hairpiece ►			▼		▼	
⌐				Gesture ►				
Stead	Vehicle for travelling on snow ►							

121

Mix 'n' Match

Pair up each of the boxes below to form the names of eight different trees and shrubs.

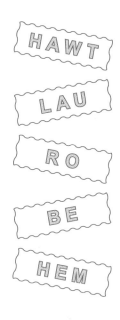

LOCK

DER

WAN

HAWT

IPER

AL

LAU

NE

JUN

RO

ECH

HORN

BE

REL

HEM

PLA

147 Round the Block

You won't need a starting block to get you under way, because it isn't a race! Just arrange the six-letter solutions to the clues into the six blocks around each clue number. Write the answers in a clockwise or anticlockwise direction and you'll find that the last answer fits into the first; the main problem will be to decide in which square to put the first letter of each word…

When read in a clockwise direction (not necessarily starting at either of the topmost squares), the letters in the pale green squares spell out the name of a bird.

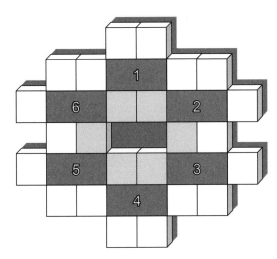

1 Taken without permission

2 Dedicate, use entirely for a specific reason

3 Part of a garment which covers the arm

4 Looked searchingly

5 Treat with excessive indulgence

6 Package

148 Casting Shadows

Which one of the shadows is that of the tractor shown here?

A

B

C

D

E

F

149 The Bottom Line

The bottom line of this grid is waiting to be filled. Every square in the solution contains only one symbol from rows 1 to 4 above, although two or more squares in the solution may contain the same symbol. At the end of every numbered row is a score, which shows:

1 the number of symbols placed in the correct finishing position on the bottom line, as indicated by a tick; and

2 the number of symbols which appear on the bottom line, but in a different position, as indicated by a cross.

Can you fill each square with the correct symbol?

					Score
1	🐰	🦇	🦗	🦢	X X
2	🦗	🕷	🐸	🦗	X X X
3	🦢	🍄	🦗	🦗	X X X
4	🍄	🕷	🐦	🐸	X X
					✓✓✓✓

124

150 Spidoku

Each of the eight segments of the spider's web should be filled with a different number from 1 to 8, in such a way that every ring also contains a different number from 1 to 8.
The segments run from the outside of the spider's web to the centre, and the rings run all the way around.
Some numbers are already in place. Can you fill in the rest?

6
7
2
8
1
3 4 6 7
3 4 8 1 4
5
3 2 4
6
5
1
1
3
2
1

151 Wordfit

Fit the listed snakes into the grid below, then rearrange the letters in the shaded squares to form the name of another snake.

3 letters
ASP
BOA

4 letters
HABU
LORA
WUTU

5 letters
ADDER
BOIGA
KRAIT
RACER
URUTU

6 letters
CANTIL
DUGITE
PYTHON
TAIPAN

9 letters
VINE SNAKE
WOLF SNAKE

10 letters
SEDGE VIPER

12 letters
TRINKET
SNAKE

Cattle Wordsearch

Find the listed breeds of cattle hidden in the grid below.
Words run in either a forward or backward direction,
horizontally, vertically or diagonally, but always in a straight line.

```
B N G K C A L B H S L E W
R S O A L D E R N E Y U B
O I O V L Z D E X T E R F
W M M L E L A T V I A N L
N M Z U A D O D V H U A I
S E A Y V T N W M W D N M
W N D H E T T A A K R K O
I T W I R S N A L Y O O U
S H G R M U R L C T F L S
S A L L O P D E R D E E I
V L U I N G T D J U R H N
B E L G I A N B L U E A S
V R N A I S E I R F H G J
```

ALDERNEY	DEXTER	LIMOUSIN
ANKOLE	DURHAM	LUING
BELGIAN BLUE	FRIESIAN	RED POLL
BRAHMAN	GALLOWAY	SHETLAND
BROWN SWISS	HEREFORD	SIMMENTHALER
CATTALO	JERSEY	WELSH BLACK
DEVON	LATVIAN	WHITE

127

Honeycomb

Place the letters of each word, one per cell, so that every word flows in a clockwise direction around a number.

Where the hexagons of one word overlap with those of another, the letter in each cell is common to both.

When finished, rearrange the letters in the pale green hexagons to form the name of a plant.

BITTEN
HORNET
INDUCT
LIQUOR

NUGGET
PENCIL
PEOPLE

PROVEN
SCURVY
UNDOES
VERIFY

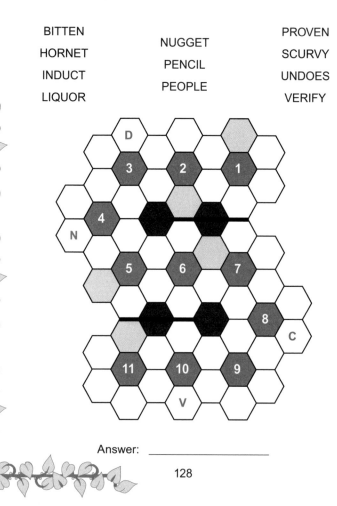

Answer: _____

154 Codeword

Every letter in this crossword has been replaced by a number, the number remaining the same for that letter wherever it occurs. Can you substitute numbers for letters and complete the crossword? One word has already been entered into the grid, to help you on your way.

When finished, use the code to spell out a bird.

	1	2	3	4	5	6	7	8	9	10	11	12	13	
A	19		20		1		21		13	6	7	12	11	N
B	3	25	3	24	3	2	5	20		2		7		O
C	5		2		25		6		23	12	22	10	2	P
D	12	22	2	12	25	6	9	3		23		12		Q
E	20		23		26		7		9	10	7	25	25	R
F		21		7		1	22	17		7		7		S
G	21	5	23	2	15	23		22	18	2	7	2	8	T
H		6		12		16	7	4		8		8		U
I	23	14	23	10	5		2		17		9		21	V
J		7		3		23	19	19	25	6	3 E	2	5	W
K	7	9	3	23	25		22		23		24 V		23	X
L		25		21		12	10	23	12	11	7 I	2	8	Y
M	17	26	5	3	21		16		11		25 L		3	Z

1	2	3 E	4	5	6	7 I	8	9	10	11	12	13
14	15	16	17	18	19	20	21	22	23	24 V	25 L	26

Answer

2	6	5	20	23	5	12	20

129

155 Wordladder

Change one letter at a time (but not the position of any letter) to make a new word – and move from the word at the top of the ladder to the word at the bottom using the exact number of rungs provided.

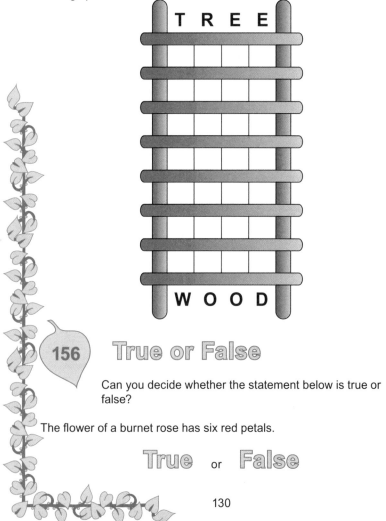

T R E E

W O O D

156 True or False

Can you decide whether the statement below is true or false?

The flower of a burnet rose has six red petals.

True or False

130

Petal Puzzle

How many words of three or more letters can you make from those on the petals, without using plurals, abbreviations or proper nouns? The central letter must appear once in every word and no letter may be used more than once unless it is on a different petal. There is at least one nine-letter word to be found.

_____

_____

_____

_____

_____

_____

_____

158 Forested Areas

Fit the letters F, O, R, E, S and T into the grid in such a way that each horizontal row, each vertical column and each of the heavily outlined sections of six squares contains a different letter. Some letters are already in place.

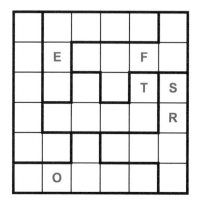

159 Herpetological Tracker

Starting at the top left corner and ending at the bottom right, track a path from letter to letter, in any direction except diagonally, in order to find the hidden reptiles and amphibians. All of the letters must be used once only.

P	Y	T	A	L	A	M	A	N	R	T	O	R	I	S	O	B
C	O	H	S	A	U	G	I	D	E	A	B	T	O	E	C	R
O	R	O	A	N	M	E	D	A	O	T	M	A	D	E	G	A
D	C	N	C	H	A	L	E	O	N	A	A	M	N	C	K	O
I	R	O	T	I	L	L	A	E	L	N	A	C	O	A	R	K
L	E	R	A	G	N	N	T	S	T	R	U	T	T	I	R	O
E	T	R	A	P	I	E	W	K	I	N	K	A	S	P	F	G

132

Anagram Mountain

Correctly solve the anagrams each step of the way from the top to the bottom of the mountain and the name of a bird will be revealed in the central column of bricks.

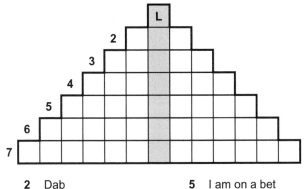

2	Dab	5	I am on a bet
3	Maple	6	Customers in
4	Two less	7	Her poor charge

161

Spelling Bee

Which is the only one of the following to be correctly spelled?

a   SANDALINE

b   SANDERLINE

c   SANDERLING

d   SANDELING

Find the correct answer to each question from the four alternatives.

1 What kind of creature is a Bombay duck?
   a. Fish   **b.** Duck
   c. Lobster   **d.** Swan

2 What is the alternative name for the gnu?
   a. Hartebeest   **b.** Wildebeest
   c. Gazelle   **d.** Warthog

3 Which animal is sometimes called a coney?
   a. Hare   **b.** Fox
   c. Rabbit   **d.** Badger

4 What mineral is commonly known as 'fool's gold'?
   a. Iron pyrite   **b.** Red oxide
   c. Haematite   **d.** Sphalerite

5 What is the usual term to describe permanently frozen subsoil?
   a. Steppe   **b.** Tundra
   c. Taiga   **d.** Permafrost

6 The skin of which animal is used to produce traditional Moroccan leather?
   a. Camel   **b.** Horse
   c. Goat   **d.** Sheep

7 Which wild animal has the Latin name of *Canis lupus*?
   a. Fox   **b.** Wolf
   c. Bear   **d.** Badger

8 Which breed of dog can run the fastest?
   a. Deer hound   **b.** Border collie
   c. Greyhound   **d.** Lurcher

Keyword Crossword

Solve the crossword puzzle in the usual way, then rearrange the letters in the shaded squares to spell out a keyword: the name of a creature.

Across

1 Punctuation mark (5)
4 Short-lived (5)
7 Reeling sensation (7)
8 Be unwell (3)
9 Coated thickly (5)
12 Deviating from the truth (5)
13 Metal-bearing mineral (3)
14 Of the kidneys (5)
15 Appetising (5)
18 Marry (3)
19 Rumour (7)
20 Country of the Arabian Peninsula (5)
21 Mooring (5)

Down

2 Drama set to music (5)
3 Unit of length (5)
4 Brochure (7)
5 Slanted letters (7)
6 Person who is gullible and easy to take advantage of (4,3)
9 Seeds used to flavour a traditional seedcake (7)
10 Realm (7)
11 Intelligent sea animal (7)
16 Correspond (5)
17 Grilled bread (5)

164 Whirlpool

Find a route for the fish to take in order to escape from the middle of the whirlpool to the calmer waters beyond.

136

Plant Sudoku

Every row, every column and each of the nine smaller boxes of nine squares should be filled with a different number from 1 to 9 inclusive. Some numbers are already in place. When the grid is completely filled, decode the numbers in the shaded squares to spell out the name of a plant. Every row should be read from left to right, starting from the top and working to the bottom of the grid.

9	3		5			7		
		2			8		3	9
		7	4					
	2				9			
3		5				8		6
			2				7	
					7	1		
8	4		1			2		
		1			4		8	3

Code

1	2	3	4	5	6	7	8	9
R	S	U	F	V	E	W	N	D

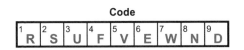

Answer: _____

137

166 Shape-up

Every row and column in this grid originally contained one bird, one flower, one leaf, one mushroom and two blank squares, although not necessarily in that order. Every symbol with a black arrow refers to the first of the four symbols encountered in the direction of the arrow. Every symbol with a white arrow refers to the second of the four symbols encountered in the direction of the arrow. Can you complete the original grid?

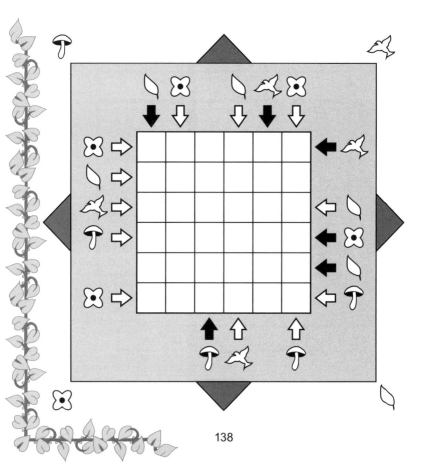

Round Dozen

First solve the clues. All of the solutions end with the letter in the middle of the circle, and in every word an additional letter is in place. When the puzzle is complete, you can then go on to discover two artists who loved the countryside, reading clockwise around the green ring of letters.

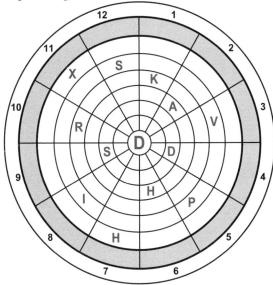

1 Facing toward the rear

2 Strived to equal or match, especially by imitating

3 Radio frequency

4 Considered as part of something

5 Caught

6 Dubbed

7 Country formerly known as Siam

8 Put into service

9 Let go

10 Told

11 Anticipated

12 Explained or answered

Answer: _____ and _____

Natural Selection

Find the correct answer to each question from the four alternatives.

1 What distinguishes the female caribou from all other female species of reindeer?
  a. Wide shoulders **b.** Long tail
  c. Uncloven hoofs **d.** Antlers

2 What kind of creature is a natterjack?
  a. Toad **b.** Frog
  c. Lizard **d.** Snake

3 What is the only marsupial native to North America?
  a. Opossum **b.** Squirrel glider
  c. Bandicoot **d.** Numbat

4 How many compartments do the stomachs of cows have?
  a. Four **b.** Two
  c. Three **d.** Five

5 The intake or absorption of what causes flamingos to turn pink?
  a. Water **b.** Iron
  c. Salt **d.** Food

6 In which of these places in the British Isles is there an area of ancient volcanic activity which is now a World Heritage site?
  a. Edinburgh **b.** Land's End
  c. Sark **d.** Staffa

7 How many wings has a ladybird?
  a. Eight **b.** Two
  c. Four **d.** Six

8 To which class of animals does the scorpion belong?
  a. Formicidae **b.** Arachnida
  c. Coleoptera **d.** Lepidoptera

Pine Forest

The object of this puzzle is to trace a single path from the top left square to the bottom right square of the grid, moving through all of the cells in either a horizontal, vertical or diagonal direction. Every cell must be entered once only and your path should take you through the letters in the sequence P-I-N-E-P-I-N-E, etc. Can you find the logical way through?

P	I	N	I	I	P	E	N
P	N	E	P	N	P	I	N
E	I	P	E	E	P	I	E
N	E	N	I	N	I	E	P
I	P	P	N	E	N	P	I
E	N	I	E	P	N	E	N
N	E	I	I	P	I	E	N
I	P	P	E	N	P	I	E

170 What's It Worth?

Each symbol stands for a different number. In order to reach the correct total at the end of each row and column, what is the value of the bat, frog, rabbit and starfish?

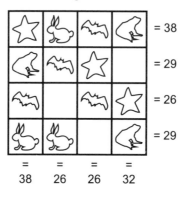

☆ star	rabbit	bat	frog	= 38
frog	bat	star		= 29
bat		bat	star	= 26
rabbit	rabbit		frog	= 29
= 38	= 26	= 26	= 32	

171 Shape Spotter

Which is the only shape to appear twice in exactly the same shading (black, white or green) in the box below? You'll need a keen eye for this one, as some shapes overlap others!

142

172 Riddle-Me-Ree

Find one letter per line, following the clues given in the verse below. For example, 'My first is in houses, but never in homes' gives the letter U as the first letter. When you have finished, the letters will spell another word.

My first is in ORCHARD, but not seen in TREE,

My second's in FIVE, though it's never in THREE,

My third is in TEDDY, but never in BEAR,

My fourth is in REINDEER, and also in HARE,

My fifth is in DRESS, but not found in SUIT,

My whole is a drink that is made from a fruit.

1st	2nd	3rd	4th	5th

173 True or False

Can you decide whether the statement below is true or false?

Tarantulas have a hard exoskeleton to protect them from predators.

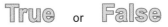

True or **False**

Telephone Code

Use the telephone dial in order to spell out a quotation attributed to John Muir.

3 9 3 7 0 1 6 2 0   6 3 3 2 8   1 3 1 9 8 0   1 8

9 3 5 5   1 8   1 7 3 1 2 ,   6 5 1 2 3 8   8 6

6 5 1 0   4 6   1 6 2   6 7 1 0   4 6 ,   9 4 3 7 3

6 1 8 9 7 3   5 1 0   4 3 1 5   1 6 2   3 4 9 3

8 8 7 3 6 3 8 4   8 6   1 6 2 0   1 6 2   8 6 9 5 .

NNR Arroword

Place the answers in the direction shown by the arrows for each clue. When finished, the letters in the green squares can be rearranged to spell out the name of a National Nature Reserve in Kent.

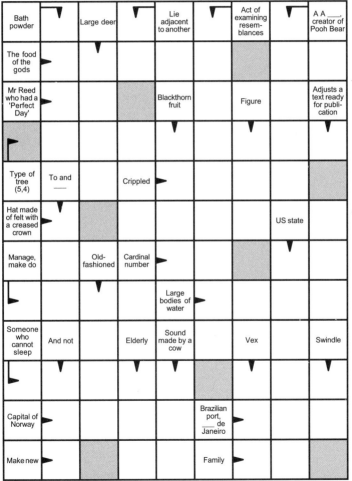

Bath powder	▼	Large deer	▼	Lie adjacent to another	▼	Act of examining resemblances	▼	A A ___, creator of Pooh Bear
The food of the gods ▶	▼							
Mr Reed who had a 'Perfect Day' ▶				Blackthorn fruit		Figure		Adjusts a text ready for publication
▶				▼		▼		▼
Type of tree (5,4)	To and ___		Crippled ▶					
Hat made of felt with a creased crown ▶	▼						US state	
Manage, make do		Old-fashioned	Cardinal number ▶				▼	
◣	▼		Large bodies of water ▶					
Someone who cannot sleep	And not		Elderly	Sound made by a cow		Vex		Swindle
◣	▼		▼	▼		▼	▼	
Capital of Norway ▶				Brazilian port, ___ de Janeiro ▶				
Make new ▶					Family ▶			

145

176 Mix 'n' Match

Pair up each of the boxes below to form the names of eight different flowers.

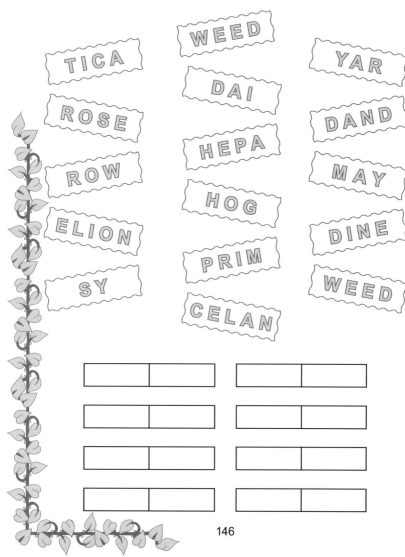

WEED

TICA

YAR

DAI

ROSE

DAND

HEPA

ROW

MAY

HOG

ELION

DINE

PRIM

SY

WEED

CELAN

146

177 Round the Block

You won't need a starting block to get you under way, because it isn't a race! Just arrange the six-letter solutions to the clues into the six blocks around each clue number. Write the answers in a clockwise or anticlockwise direction and you'll find that the last answer fits into the first; the main problem will be to decide in which square to put the first letter of each word…

When read in a clockwise direction (not necessarily starting at either of the topmost squares), the letters in the pale green squares spell out the name of a plant.

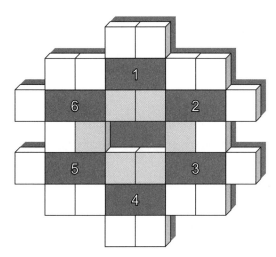

1 Number, XC in Roman numerals

2 Hat made of felt, with a creased crown

3 Prince ___, Queen Victoria's consort

4 Christian celebration of the Resurrection of Christ

5 Most peculiar

6 Handsome youth loved by both Aphrodite and Persephone

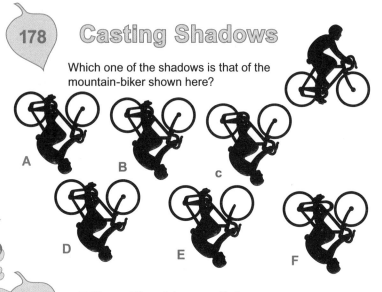

178 Casting Shadows

Which one of the shadows is that of the mountain-biker shown here?

A

B

C

D

E

F

179 The Bottom Line

The bottom line of this grid is waiting to be filled. Every square in the solution contains only one symbol from rows 1 to 5 above, although two or more squares in the solution may contain the same symbol. At the end of every numbered row is a score, which shows:

1 the number of symbols placed in the correct finishing position on the bottom line, as indicated by a tick; and

2 the number of symbols which appear on the bottom line, but in a different position, as indicated by a cross.

Can you fill each square with the correct symbol?

				Score
1				✓
2				✗
3				✗ ✗
4				✓ ✗
5				✓ ✗
				✓✓✓✓

148

180 Spidoku

Each of the eight segments of the spider's web should be filled with a different number from 1 to 8, in such a way that every ring also contains a different number from 1 to 8.
The segments run from the outside of the spider's web to the centre, and the rings run all the way around.
Some numbers are already in place. Can you fill in the rest?

Wordfit

Fit the listed British rivers into the grid below, then rearrange the letters in the shaded squares to form the name of another British river.

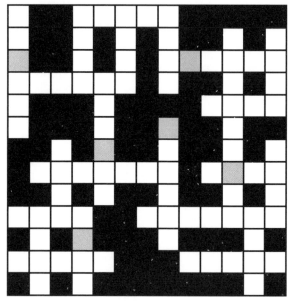

4 letters
AVON
DART
EDEN
LUNE
NENE
TAFF
TEES
TEST
TOWY
TYNE

WEAR
YARE

5 letters
DOVEY
TEIFI
TRENT

6 letters
MEDWAY
MERSEY

RIBBLE
SEVERN
WHARFE

7 letters
PARRETT
WELLAND

9 letters
GREAT OUSE

Birdsearch

Find the listed birds hidden in the grid below. Words run in either a forward or backward direction, horizontally, vertically or diagonally, but always in a straight line.

```
W K R A L Y K S Q M G W S
S P A R R O W A D K C A J
C U J I E V N E H R O O M
R F S I E T I K D E R U E
O F B U Z Z A R D U R G U
S I U M F R O W Y M D O L
S N L E E Y E E R I Y I N
B S L O O R R D R A A P H
I I F P J P L T S U E J B
L S I O S B R I Q T V H I
L K N O V A T E N N A G S
C I C H P I G E O N Z R S
J N H O O D E D C R O W T
```

BULLFINCH	JACKDAW	QUAIL
BUZZARD	MERLIN	RED KITE
CROSSBILL	MOORHEN	REDSTART
GANNET	OSPREY	SHEARWATER
HERON	PARTRIDGE	SISKIN
HOODED CROW	PIGEON	SKYLARK
HOOPOE	PUFFIN	SPARROW

183 Honeycomb

Place the letters of each word, one per cell, so that every word flows in a clockwise direction around a number.

Where the hexagons of one word overlap with those of another, the letter in each cell is common to both.

When finished, rearrange the letters in the pale green hexagons to form the name of a bird.

BUCKLE

CHORUS

CUDGEL

CURFEW

GOBLET

LENGTH

NEREID

PARADE

PARENT

TALKIE

WEAPON

D

3 2 1

4

5 6 7

A

D

8

11 10 9

C

Answer: _____

184 Codeword

Every letter in this crossword has been replaced by a number, the number remaining the same for that letter wherever it occurs. Can you substitute numbers for letters and complete the crossword? One word has already been entered into the grid, to help you on your way.

When finished, use the code to spell out a plant.

	1	2	3	4	5	6	7	8	9	10	11	12	13
A	8	1	15	10		21	17	7	16	1	4	14	25
B	25		7		20		12		18		7		4
C	6	25	17	21	24	7	16		9	10	12	8	2
D	4		9		18		15		1		20		23
E	14	24 R	7 A	5 V	1 E		1	7	24	10	26	2	
F	7				5		24				10		5
G	9	26	25	5	1	17		1	4	13	2	16	1
H	10		5				9		7				26
I		22	7	14	3	7	17		19	18	11	12	1
J	9		10		4		1		3		12		16
K	14	26	18	4	7		1	19	18	9	25	8	1
L	7		25		5		5		4		10		4
M	16	7	4	4	1	24	1	8		5	1	9	10

N O P Q R S T U V W X Y Z

1 E	2	3	4	5 V	6	7 A	8	9	10	11	12	13
14	15	16	17	18	19	20	21	22	23	24 R	25	26

Answer

26	25	4	1	2	9	12	14	3	17	1

185 Wordladder

Change one letter at a time (but not the position of any letter) to make a new word – and move from the word at the top of the ladder to the word at the bottom using the exact number of rungs provided.

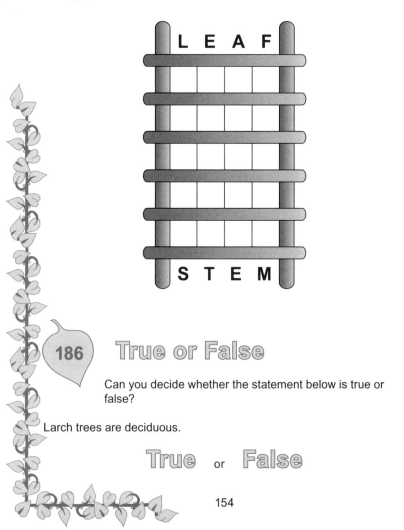

L E A F

S T E M

186 True or False

Can you decide whether the statement below is true or false?

Larch trees are deciduous.

True or False

Petal Puzzle

How many words of three or more letters can you make from those on the petals, without using plurals, abbreviations or proper nouns? The central letter must appear once in every word and no letter may be used more than once unless it is on a different petal. There is at least one nine-letter word to be found.

T U

P B

U

R E

C T

_____
_____
_____
_____
_____
_____
_____

188 Forested Areas

Fit the letters F, O, R, E, S and T into the grid in such a way that each horizontal row, each vertical column and each of the heavily outlined sections of six squares contains a different letter. Some letters are already in place.

		E			F
T	S				
			R		
				O	

189 Moth Tracker

Starting at the top left corner and ending at the bottom right, track a path from letter to letter, in any direction except diagonally, in order to find the hidden moths. All of the letters must be used once only.

L	E	O	P	E	R	O	R	C	I	N	N	A	B	O	R	N
P	A	P	M	W	A	H	G	R	E	T	S	E	A	H	U	P
O	V	A	E	K	E	R	O	A	T	F	O	R	R	T	G	F
U	R	R	D	P	G	I	T	T	E	N	R	U	P	E	O	O
R	E	T	S	L	U	M	E	M	A	N	G	B	U	N	T	M
E	L	U	B	O	L	E	I	P	G	O	H	S	S	I	M	A
R	P	S	I	A	G	H	O	S	T	L	O	R	N	E	R	N

156

Anagram Mountain

Correctly solve the anagrams each step of the way from the top to the bottom of the mountain and the name of a marine creature will be revealed in the central column of bricks.

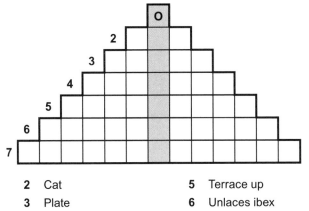

2	Cat	5	Terrace up
3	Plate	6	Unlaces ibex
4	Eroding	7	Aristocrat pen

191

Spelling Bee

Which is the only one of the following to be correctly spelled?

- a AVOCET
- b AVACET
- c ADVACET
- d ADVOCET

Natural Selection

Find the correct answer to each question from the four alternatives.

1 What colour are the petals of the Burnet rose?
  a. Cream   **b.** Red
  c. Pink   **d.** Rust

2 *Bellis perennis* is the Latin name of which common field flower?
  a. Buttercup   **b.** Cornflower
  c. Cowslip   **d.** Daisy

3 Which is the highest point in England and Wales?
  a. Cader Idris   **b.** Scafell Pike
  c. Helvellyn   **d.** Snowdon

4 The berry-like cones of which common tree are used to flavour gin?
  a. Cedar   **b.** Willow
  c. Spruce   **d.** Juniper

5 The larva of which creature causes a jumping bean to jump?
  a. Moth   **b.** Beetle
  c. Butterfly   **d.** Wasp

6 In Norse mythology, two of which kind of bird were the servants of Odin?
  a. Eagle   **b.** Raven
  c. Heron   **d.** Buzzard

7 The whimbrel is a species of which kind of bird?
  a. Pigeon   **b.** Dove
  c. Thrush   **d.** Curlew

8 After humans, which land mammals live the longest?
  a. Polar bear   **b.** Hippopotamus
  c. Elephant   **d.** Gorilla

Keyword Crossword

Solve the crossword puzzle in the usual way, then rearrange the letters in the shaded squares to spell out a keyword: the name of a fish.

Across

3 Sleep (7)
7 Destitute (5)
8 Theft by threat of violence (7)
9 Small and elegant (5)
10 Item eaten on Shrove Tuesday (7)
13 Refuse to do business with (7)
17 Line of travel (5)
18 Non-attendance (7)
20 Left over, superfluous (5)
21 Impedes the progress of (7)

Down

1 Refuses to acknowledge (5)
2 Lying under oath (7)
3 Sweet sticky liquid (5)
4 Characteristic of a city (5)
5 Four-winged insect (3)
6 Piece of poetry (5)
11 Social insect (3)
12 Shaped like a ring (7)
13 Shore (5)
14 One sixteenth of a pound (5)
15 Lock of hair (5)
16 Cap with no brim or peak (5)
19 Earth's nearest star (3)

194 Whirlpool

Find a route for the fish to take in order to escape from the middle of the whirlpool to the calmer waters beyond.

Geographical Sudoku

Every row, every column and each of the nine smaller boxes of nine squares should be filled with a different number from 1 to 9 inclusive. Some numbers are already in place. When the grid is completely filled, decode the numbers in the shaded squares to spell out the name of a range of hills. Every row should be read from left to right, starting from the top and working to the bottom of the grid.

			7				9	1
					9			5
		8		3			2	
		9	1					
7			3		4			2
					5	3		
	4			7		6		
2			9					
9	3				6			

Code

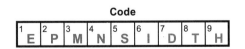

1	2	3	4	5	6	7	8	9
E	P	M	N	S	I	D	T	H

Answer: _____

196 Shape-up

Every row and column in this grid originally contained one bird, one flower, one leaf, one mushroom and two blank squares, although not necessarily in that order. Every symbol with a black arrow refers to the first of the four symbols encountered in the direction of the arrow. Every symbol with a white arrow refers to the second of the four symbols encountered in the direction of the arrow. Can you complete the original grid?

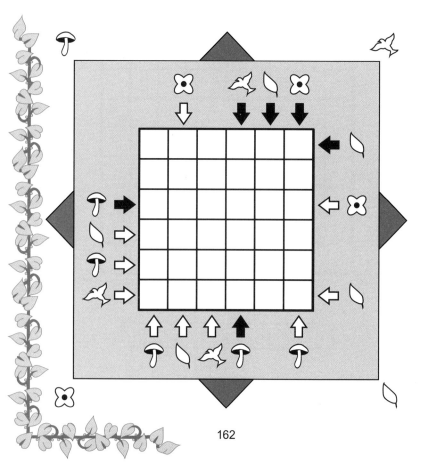

Round Dozen

197

First solve the clues. All of the solutions end with the letter in the middle of the circle, and in every word an additional letter is in place. When the puzzle is complete, you can then go on to discover two plants, reading clockwise around the green ring of letters.

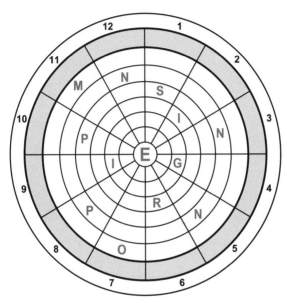

1 Drivel

2 Entitled, qualified

3 'Arm' of an octopus

4 Three-sided figure

5 Women's underwear and nightclothes

6 Surround, gird

7 Put up with

8 Vulnerability to the elements

9 State capital of South Australia

10 Startle

11 Appropriate (especially money) fraudulently to one's own use

12 Idiom

Answer: _____ and _____

Find the correct answer to each question from the four alternatives.

1 Of what family of animals is the Poison dart, from which some South American natives extract a poison for arrow-tips?
  a. Snake   **b.** Frog
  c. Lizard   **d.** Cat

2 The term *Chiroptera* refers to which kinds of animals?
  a. Beetles   **b.** Moths
  c. Starfish   **d.** Bats

3 Which animal is not a member of the Mustelid family?
  a. Pine marten   **b.** Mink
  c. Beaver   **d.** Otter

4 Which is the largest living rodent?
  a. Capybara   **b.** Agouti
  c. Nutria   **d.** Coypu

5 How many walls has a Dutch barn in the UK?
  a. Four   **b.** Three
  c. Two   **d.** None

6 With a wingspan of up to 16", which is Britain's largest bat?
  a. Noctule   **b.** Long-eared
  c. Greater horseshoe **d.** Natterer's bat

7 What is a Miller's thumb?
  a. Grasshopper   **b.** Large fly
  c. Mill wheel   **d.** Freshwater fish

8 At up to 35 feet in length, what is the largest fish to normally be found in inshore waters of the British Isles?
  a. Porbeagle shark **b.** Thresher shark
  c. Basking shark   **d.** Blue shark

199 Pine Forest

The object of this puzzle is to trace a single path from the top left square to the bottom right square of the grid, moving through all of the cells in either a horizontal, vertical or diagonal direction. Every cell must be entered once only and your path should take you through the letters in the sequence P-I-N-E-P-I-N-E, etc. Can you find the logical way through?

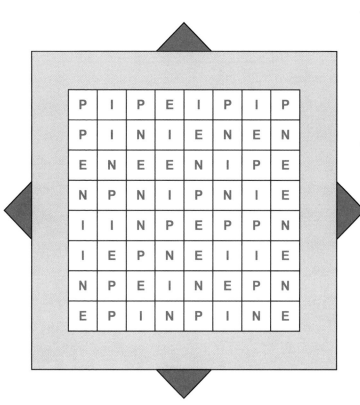

P	I	P	E	I	P	I	P
P	I	N	I	E	N	E	N
E	N	E	E	N	I	P	E
N	P	N	I	P	N	I	E
I	I	N	P	E	P	P	N
I	E	P	N	E	I	I	E
N	P	E	I	N	E	P	N
E	P	I	N	P	I	N	E

200 What's It Worth?

Each symbol stands for a different number. In order to reach the correct total at the end of each row and column, what is the value of the bat, frog, rabbit and starfish?

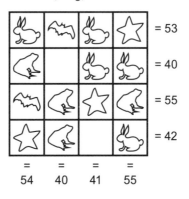

201 Shape Spotter

Which is the only shape to appear twice in exactly the same shading (black, white or green) in the box below? You'll need a keen eye for this one, as some shapes overlap others!

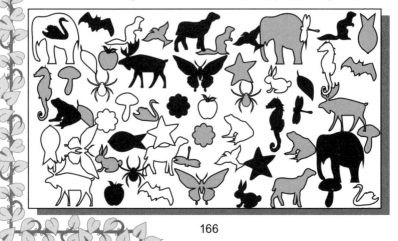

166

202 Riddle-Me-Ree

Find one letter per line, following the clues given in the verse below. For example, 'My first is in houses, but never in homes' gives the letter U as the first letter. When you have finished, the letters will spell another word.

My first is in ASTER, and also in ROSE,

My second's in HEEL, but it's not seen in TOES,

My third is in FOREST, and also in TREES,

My fourth is in HIVES, as well as in BEES,

My fifth is in PERIL, though never in HARM,

My whole is an animal seen on a farm.

1st	2nd	3rd	4th	5th

203 True or False

Can you decide whether the statement below is true or false?

The Japanese spider crab has a leg span measuring up to 3.7 metres (12 feet).

True   or   False

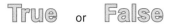

Telephone Code

Use the telephone dial in order to spell out a quotation attributed to Gilbert White.

1 1 8 8   2 7 4 6 4   6 6   8 4 3   9 4 6 3 ,   5 4 4 3

8 9 1 5 5 6 9 8 ,   1 0   8 4 6 6 4 6 3   8 4 3

8 9 7 3 1 2 3 ,   1 8   8 4 3 0   6 5 1 0   6 9 3 7

6 6 6 5 8   1 6 2   8 8 7 3 1 5 8 .

205

NNR Arroword

Place the answers in the direction shown by the arrows for each clue. When finished, the letters in the green squares can be rearranged to spell out the name of a National Nature Reserve in Aberdeenshire.

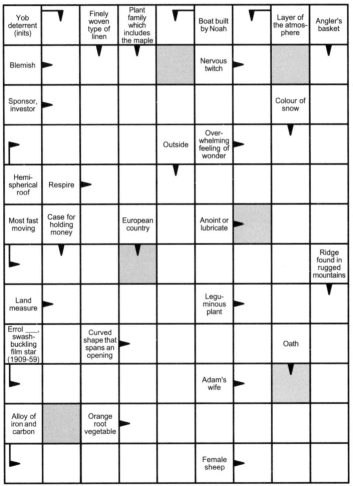

169

Mix 'n' Match

Pair up each of the boxes below to form the names of eight different birds.

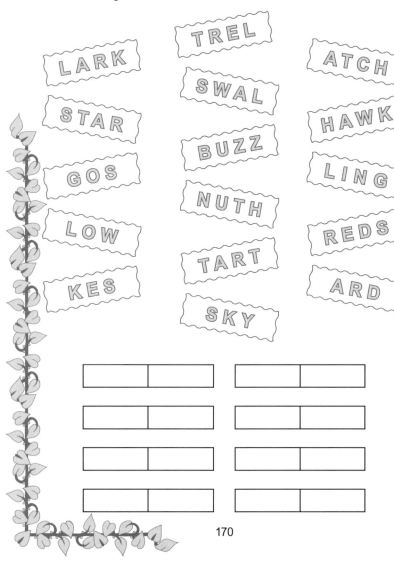

LARK

TREL

ATCH

STAR

SWAL

HAWK

GOS

BUZZ

LING

LOW

NUTH

REDS

KES

TART

ARD

SKY

170

Round the Block

You won't need a starting block to get you under way, because it isn't a race! Just arrange the six-letter solutions to the clues into the six blocks around each clue number. Write the answers in a clockwise or anticlockwise direction and you'll find that the last answer fits into the first; the main problem will be to decide in which square to put the first letter of each word…

When read in a clockwise direction (not necessarily starting at either of the topmost squares), the letters in the pale green squares spell out the name of a creature.

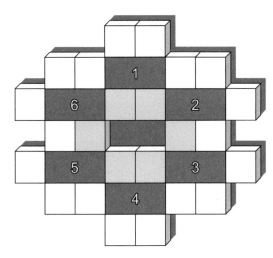

1 Young cat

2 Hinder or prevent

3 Beetle considered divine by ancient Egyptians

4 Large terrestrial monkey, with a dog-like muzzle

5 Decorative strip of material

6 Woman's two-piece bathing costume

Casting Shadows

Which one of the shadows is that of the sprig of blossom shown here?

A B C

D E F

The Bottom Line

The bottom line of this grid is waiting to be filled. Every square in the solution contains only one symbol from rows 1 to 5 above, although two or more squares in the solution may contain the same symbol. At the end of every numbered row is a score, which shows:

1. the number of symbols placed in the correct finishing position on the bottom line, as indicated by a tick; and

2. the number of symbols which appear on the bottom line, but in a different position, as indicated by a cross.

Can you fill each square with the correct symbol?

				Score
1				✗
2				✓✓
3				✗✗
4				✗✗
5				✗✗
				✓✓✓✓

210 Spidoku

Each of the eight segments of the spider's web should be filled with a different number from 1 to 8, in such a way that every ring also contains a different number from 1 to 8.
The segments run from the outside of the spider's web to the centre, and the rings run all the way around.
Some numbers are already in place. Can you fill in the rest?

211 Wordfit

Fit the listed trees and shrubs into the grid below, then rearrange the letters in the shaded squares to form the name of another tree or shrub.

3 letters
YEW

4 letters
ACER
DATE
DEAL
LIME
PEAR
PLUM

5 letters
ABELE
ALDER
APPLE
BEECH
BROOM
ELDER
PEACH
THUJA

6 letters
ACACIA
ORANGE
PAWPAW
POPLAR

9 letters
JACARANDA
ZEBRA WOOD

12 letters
WELLINGTONIA

212 Fishing Wordsearch

Find the listed fishing words hidden in the grid below.
Words run in either a forward or backward direction,
horizontally, vertically or diagonally, but always in a straight line.

A	Q	Y	G	X	Y	P	W	P	E	C	P	V
G	E	C	Y	H	P	N	R	O	T	U	E	D
N	M	R	S	H	O	A	N	A	N	J	R	O
I	C	H	U	B	C	S	I	U	W	N	E	R
L	F	M	V	L	R	R	T	L	T	N	I	Y
D	N	R	E	T	S	Y	O	S	F	J	P	M
O	M	M	E	H	E	K	O	O	H	O	M	K
C	B	P	A	K	F	A	A	H	F	A	Y	P
I	O	D	E	L	E	E	S	T	U	A	R	Y
T	B	P	U	K	C	R	E	M	E	Z	R	K
K	Z	A	G	L	D	Y	P	F	J	U	A	P
F	G	Q	S	A	P	M	I	R	H	S	P	G
P	C	X	B	S	R	E	A	R	I	P	W	I

BASS	GHOST SHARK	PRAWN
CARP	HOOK	SEPIA
CHUB	LURE	SHAD
CLAM	MINNOW	SHRIMP
CODLING	OYSTER	SKATE
DORY	PARR	TOPE
ESTUARY	PIER	TUNNY

213 Honeycomb

Place the letters of each word, one per cell, so that every word flows in a clockwise direction around a number.

Where the hexagons of one word overlap with those of another, the letter in each cell is common to both.

When finished, rearrange the letters in the pale green hexagons to form the name of a national park.

ARCTIC

CLOSET

DEMURE

GOLDEN

GYRATE

NEURAL

SEAMEN

TALLOW

TAXING

VELLUM

WATERY

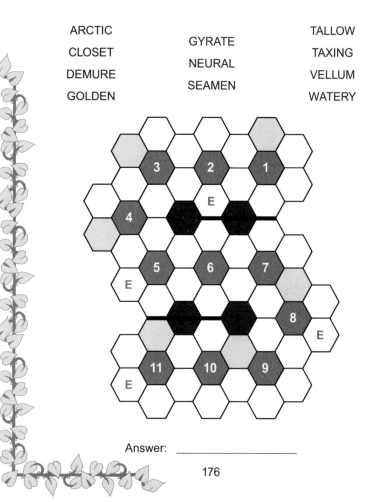

Answer: _____

214 Codeword

Every letter in this crossword has been replaced by a number, the number remaining the same for that letter wherever it occurs. Can you substitute numbers for letters and complete the crossword? One word has already been entered into the grid, to help you on your way.

When finished, use the code to spell out a plant.

A	16	12	15	21	12	8	9	■	11	1	22	8	19
B	12	■	3	■	8	■	1	5	24	■	25	■	3
C	10	24	22	8	25	15	13	■	12	8	22	3	15
D	1	■	20	■	22	■	13	■	25	■	3	■	25
E	3	24	19	24	3	■	24	10	19	24	20	22	25
F	■	4	■	■	15	25	20	2	■	■	15	■	15
G	10	12	10	1	5	1	■	25	17	1	3	15	25
H	17	■	24	■	■	3	1	19	15	■	■	1	■
					R	**A**	**T**	**E**				
I	15	14	10	13	1	12	23	■	13	12	7	19	25
J	26	■	18	■	10	■	4	■	20	■	22	■	15
K	22	20	20	15	3	■	22	8	7	1	6	15	5
L	15	■	12	■	12	19	25	■	22	■	6	■	1
M	25	12	19	15	5	■	17	1	13	10	2	24	8

N O P Q R S T U V W X Y Z

1 A	2	3 R	4	5	6	7	8	9	10	11	12	13
14	15 E	16	17	18	19 T	20	21	22	23	24	25	26

Answer

7	24	14	9	13	24	16	15

215 Wordladder

Change one letter at a time (but not the position of any letter) to make a new word – and move from the word at the top of the ladder to the word at the bottom using the exact number of rungs provided.

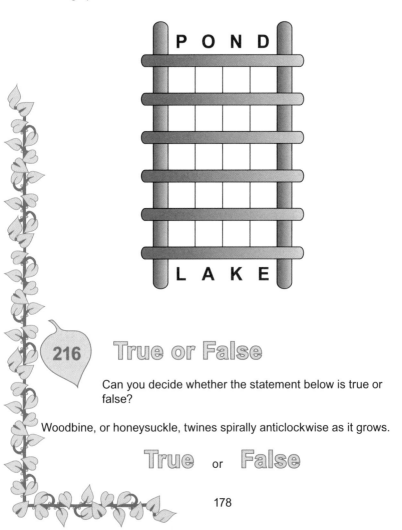

P O N D

L A K E

216 True or False

Can you decide whether the statement below is true or false?

Woodbine, or honeysuckle, twines spirally anticlockwise as it grows.

True or False

Petal Puzzle

How many words of three or more letters can you make from those on the petals, without using plurals, abbreviations or proper nouns? The central letter must appear once in every word and no letter may be used more than once unless it is on a different petal. There is at least one nine-letter word to be found.

_____

_____

_____

_____

_____

_____

_____

218 Forested Areas

Fit the letters F, O, R, E, S and T into the grid in such a way that each horizontal row, each vertical column and each of the heavily outlined sections of six squares contains a different letter. Some letters are already in place.

E					F
	S				
	T				
		R			
		O			

219 Bird Tracker

Starting at the top left corner and ending at the bottom right, track a path from letter to letter, in any direction except diagonally, in order to find the hidden birds. All of the letters must be used once only.

T	H	R	O	G	O	O	S	A	G	E	R	K	G	R	O	U
C	A	U	O	K	C	S	E	M	P	I	O	O	T	R	A	S
K	L	S	E	C	U	W	A	N	R	G	N	I	R	I	P	E
B	B	H	V	O	D	H	C	E	E	H	C	F	G	D	G	O
I	R	T	F	I	E	L	N	N	C	H	A	F	E	L	E	S
R	D	R	A	A	F	D	I	F	T	I	R	E	H	G	A	H
E	D	S	T	R	E	B	L	U	E	T	O	N	E	A	W	K

180

220 Anagram Mountain

Correctly solve the anagrams each step of the way from the top to the bottom of the mountain and the name of a weather feature will be revealed in the central column of bricks.

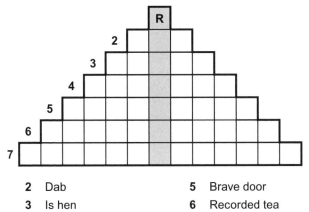

2	Dab	5	Brave door
3	Is hen	6	Recorded tea
4	Nero guy	7	Crews stir trip

221 Spelling Bee

Which is the only one of the following to be correctly spelled?

a   WIMBRELLE

b   WHIMBEREL

c   WIMBREL

d   WHIMBREL

181

Natural Selection

Find the correct answer to each question from the four alternatives.

1 What is a fly terret?
   a. A special fish hook **b.** A horse brass
   c. A plough **d.** A wheel

2 Now becoming rare, which is Britain's largest land beetle?
   a. Bull beetle **b.** Horse beetle
   c. Stag beetle **d.** Tanner beetle

3 What is a green drake?
   a. A duck **b.** A stagnant pond
   c. A wading bird **d.** A species of mayfly

4 The Fortingall yew is widely believed to be the oldest tree in Britain. In which Scottish county is it sited?
   a. Sutherland **b.** Argyll
   c. Banffshire **d.** Perthshire

5 Smelts are close relatives of which other fish?
   a. Salmon **b.** Cod
   c. Pike **d.** Roach

6 American, German and Dusky are all species of which insect?
   a. Ant **b.** Beetle
   c. Fly **d.** Cockroach

7 What kind of bird is a Khaki Campbell?
   a. Chicken **b.** Turkey
   c. Duck **d.** Goose

8 Which one of the following is not a native British grasshopper or cricket?
   a. Corn-ear grasshopper **b.** Large marsh grasshopper
   c. House cricket **d.** Mole cricket

Keyword Crossword

Solve the crossword puzzle in the usual way, then rearrange the letters in the shaded squares to spell out a keyword: the name of an insect.

Across

1 Annoy continually (6)
5 Rented out (3)
7 Hackney carriage (4)
8 Deprive of food (6)
9 Silvery metal (3)
10 Cuckoo pint, for example (4)
11 Offensively bold (5)
13 Artist's tripod (5)
17 Long detailed story (4)
18 Hawaiian wreath (3)
19 Pivot (6)
20 Identical (4)
21 Speck (3)
22 Absorb food (6)

Down

2 Pollen-bearing part of a flower's stamen (6)
3 To the opposite side (6)
4 Cut of meat (5)
5 Substance used as acid/alkali indicator (6)
6 Passage through or under something (6)
11 Narrative poem of popular origin (6)
12 Help (6)
14 Performing (6)
15 Overabundance (6)
16 Founded (5)

Whirlpool

Find a route for the fish to take in order to escape from the middle of the whirlpool to the calmer waters beyond.

225 Plant Sudoku

Every row, every column and each of the nine smaller boxes of nine squares should be filled with a different number from 1 to 9 inclusive. Some numbers are already in place. When the grid is completely filled, decode the numbers in the shaded squares to spell out the name of a plant. Every row should be read from left to right, starting from the top and working to the bottom of the grid.

		1				3	5	
		9		6	8			1
			1	4				9
			6	2		1		
	1	7				4	2	
		8		7	1			
7				1	6			
1			8	5		9		
	8	2				5		

Code

1	2	3	4	5	6	7	8	9
P	T	O	S	R	W	N	A	D

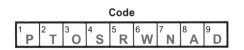

Answer: _____

185

Shape-up

Every row and column in this grid originally contained one bird, one flower, one leaf, one mushroom and two blank squares, although not necessarily in that order. Every symbol with a black arrow refers to the first of the four symbols encountered in the direction of the arrow. Every symbol with a white arrow refers to the second of the four symbols encountered in the direction of the arrow. Can you complete the original grid?

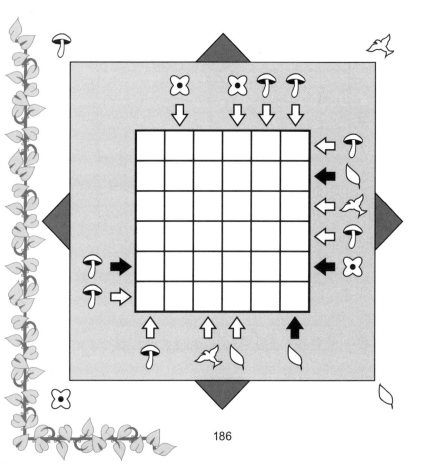

227 Round Dozen

First solve the clues. All of the solutions end with the letter in the middle of the circle, and in every word an additional letter is in place. When the puzzle is complete, you can then go on to discover a plant, reading clockwise around the green ring of letters.

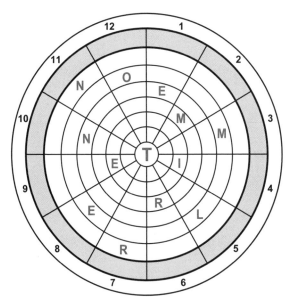

1 Filbert

2 Beat through cleverness and wit

3 Designed for consumers with high incomes

4 Author of books

5 Quietly and steadily persevering

6 County in southern England

7 Send from one place to another

8 Responsive to orders

9 Most strident or clamorous

10 Metal glove

11 Not affected by blight or corruption

12 One who frees a place or person from evil spirits

Answer: _____

Find the correct answer to each question from the four alternatives.

1 A stoat's coat turns to which colour in winter?
   a. Grey   **b.** White
   c. Black   **d.** Brown

2 What is a mountain ringlet?
   a. A sheep   **b.** A flower
   c. A goat   **d.** A butterfly

3 The great spotted woodpecker is black, white and which other colour?
   a. Red   **b.** Green
   c. Brown   **d.** Blue

4 Which common field-flower has the Latin name *Ranunculus*?
   a. Daisy   **b.** Cowslip
   c. Buttercup   **d.** Rockrose

5 Bar-tailed and Black-tailed are the two species of which bird?
   a. Grouse   **b.** Godwit
   c. Heron   **d.** Puffin

6 From which country did the Saanen goat originate?
   a. France   **b.** Belgium
   c. Italy   **d.** Switzerland

7 Landrace and Tamworth are breeds of which animal?
   a. Pig   **b.** Sheep
   c. Horse   **d.** Cattle

8 Which one of the following mushrooms is not poisonous?
   a. Panther cap   **b.** Yellow staining
   c. Fly agaric   **d.** Wood blewit

229 Pine Forest

The object of this puzzle is to trace a single path from the top left square to the bottom right square of the grid, moving through all of the cells in either a horizontal, vertical or diagonal direction. Every cell must be entered once only and your path should take you through the letters in the sequence P-I-N-E-P-I-N-E, etc. Can you find the logical way through?

P	I	E	P	E	E	I	N
I	P	N	I	N	N	P	E
N	N	E	P	I	I	P	N
N	E	I	I	N	P	E	I
E	I	P	N	P	E	I	N
P	P	N	N	E	P	I	E
E	E	I	I	E	N	I	P
N	I	P	P	E	P	N	E

230 What's It Worth?

Each symbol stands for a different number. In order to reach the correct total at the end of each row and column, what is the value of the bat, frog, rabbit and starfish?

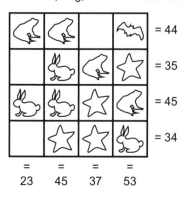

231 Shape Spotter

Which is the only shape to appear twice in exactly the same shading (black, white or green) in the box below? You'll need a keen eye for this one, as some shapes overlap others!

Riddle-Me-Ree

Find one letter per line, following the clues given in the verse below. For example, 'My first is in houses, but never in homes' gives the letter U as the first letter. When you have finished, the letters will spell another word.

My first is in FLOWER, but never in BLOOM,

My second's in FEATHER, but not seen in PLUME,

My third's not in STALK, though it is found in PETAL,

My fourth is in STEEL, as well as in METAL,

My fifth is in PADLOCK, and also in KEY,

My whole is a mollusc that lives in the sea.

1st	2nd	3rd	4th	5th

233 **True or False**

Can you decide whether the statement below is true or false?

There are about 5,000 species of mammals and 25 per cent of these are marine.

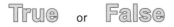

True or False

Telephone Code

Use the telephone dial in order to spell out a quotation attributed to William John Wills.

843   643366   4373   48   1   131984395

1472,   63   1   23542183   176603

265697,   846332   9484   6464   11698

843   6324,   162   843   94638   517432

9484   37336   162   697653.

NNR Arroword

Place the answers in the direction shown by the arrows for each clue. When finished, the letters in the green squares can be rearranged to spell out the name of a National Nature Reserve in Suffolk.

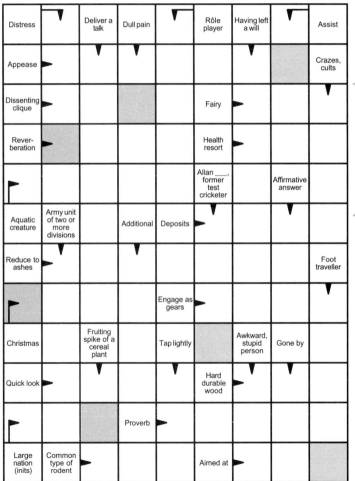

Mix 'n' Match

Pair up each of the boxes below to form the names of eight different trees.

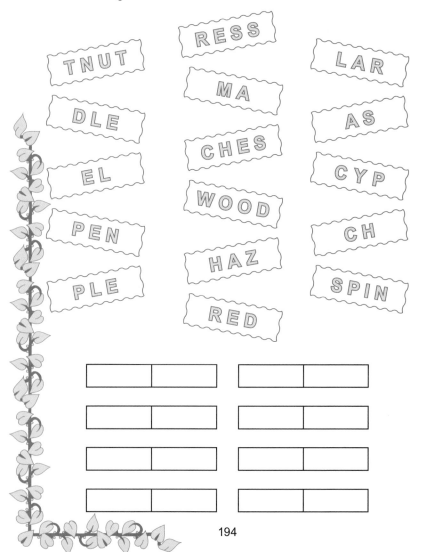

TNUT RESS LAR

DLE MA AS

EL CHES CYP

PEN WOOD CH

PLE HAZ SPIN

RED

Round the Block

You won't need a starting block to get you under way, because it isn't a race! Just arrange the six-letter solutions to the clues into the six blocks around each clue number. Write the answers in a clockwise or anticlockwise direction and you'll find that the last answer fits into the first; the main problem will be to decide in which square to put the first letter of each word…

When read in a clockwise direction (not necessarily starting at either of the topmost squares), the letters in the pale green squares spell out the name of a creature.

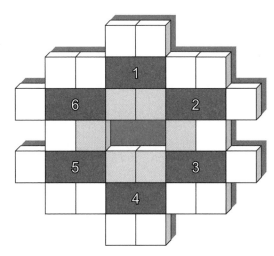

1   Small beetle that lives on plants and plant products

2   Precious stones

3   Organs of photosynthesis and transpiration

4   Wild and menacing

5   Arid land with little or no vegetation

6   Was unsuccessful

Casting Shadows

Which one of the shadows is that of the palm tree shown here?

A

B

C

D

E

F

239

The Bottom Line

The bottom line of this grid is waiting to be filled. Every square in the solution contains only one symbol from rows 1 to 5 above, although two or more squares in the solution may contain the same symbol. At the end of every numbered row is a score, which shows:

1. the number of symbols placed in the correct finishing position on the bottom line, as indicated by a tick; and

2. the number of symbols which appear on the bottom line, but in a different position, as indicated by a cross.

Can you fill each square with the correct symbol?

Score

				Score
1				X X
2				X X
3				X X
4				X X
5				X X
				✓✓✓✓

196

240 Spidoku

Each of the eight segments of the spider's web should be filled with a different number from 1 to 8, in such a way that every ring also contains a different number from 1 to 8. The segments run from the outside of the spider's web to the centre, and the rings run all the way around.

Some numbers are already in place. Can you fill in the rest?

241 Wordfit

Fit the listed Scottish lochs into the grid below, then rearrange the letters in the shaded squares to form the name of another Scottish loch.

4 letters
BUIE
FYNE
NESS
RYAN

5 letters
DUICH
ETIVE
FLEET

HUORN
LEVEN
NEVIS

6 letters
CARRON
CRERAN
CRINAN
EYNORT
LINNHE

7 letters
EISHORT
SCAVAIG

8 letters
SCRIDAIN
TORRIDON

198

Productive Wordsearch

Find the listed nuts, seeds and fruits hidden in the grid.
Words run in either a forward or backward direction,
horizontally, vertically or diagonally, but always in a straight line.

E	L	X	N	Y	Y	R	R	E	B	L	I	B
V	E	B	F	D	N	O	M	L	A	B	S	I
F	Z	L	E	T	U	N	L	A	W	R	B	L
T	A	F	D	E	V	I	L	O	F	A	L	B
X	H	Y	C	E	C	Y	S	I	L	Z	U	E
M	T	O	R	H	R	H	L	I	S	I	E	R
U	A	Y	R	R	E	B	K	C	A	L	B	Y
L	M	P	Y	J	E	R	E	O	B	N	E	R
B	A	O	Z	R	G	B	R	R	S	U	R	O
E	R	P	T	T	P	Q	N	Y	R	T	R	K
R	I	P	E	C	A	N	A	A	D	Y	Y	C
R	N	Y	W	C	O	N	K	E	R	A	N	I
Y	D	P	T	U	N	T	S	E	H	C	Y	H

ALMOND	CHESTNUT	HICKORY
BEECH	CONKER	MULBERRY
BILBERRY	CRANBERRY	OLIVE
BLACKBERRY	ELDERBERRY	PECAN
BLUEBERRY	FILBERT	POPPY
BRAZIL NUT	FLAX	TAMARIND
CHERRY	HAZEL	WALNUT

243 Honeycomb

Place the letters of each word, one per cell, so that every word flows in a clockwise direction around a number.
Where the hexagons of one word overlap with those of another, the letter in each cell is common to both.
When finished, rearrange the letters in the pale green hexagons to form the name of a season.

CREATE
GANNET
NEATER
PELLET

REPUTE
RETINA
REVILE

SECTOR
SEPTUM
SMOOTH
THENCE

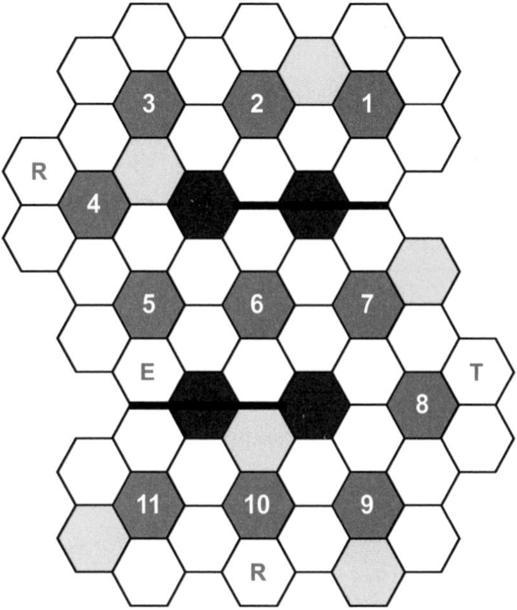

Answer: ____________________

244 Codeword

Every letter in this crossword has been replaced by a number, the number remaining the same for that letter wherever it occurs. Can you substitute numbers for letters and complete the crossword? One word has already been entered into the grid, to help you on your way.

When finished, use the code to spell out a type of moth.

	13	11	15	13	17	1	8	2		19	21	19	3
A	24		19		19		3		6		4		6
B	24		9		9	13	2	23	13		2		18
C	3	12	13	1	13		13		1	16	2	18	1
D		2			17		13		12		13		24
E	12	4	17	15		3	6	18	19	2	15		13
F		13	13	17	19	13		25	2	4	19	9	
G	26		7	16	3	13	2	25		24	1	8	20
H	18		13		2		8		14			10	
I	23	18	9	22	8		1		4	7	21	13	17 R
J	19		19		1	19	12	5	13		4		13 E
K	8		8		9		13		4		2		1 N
L	2	19	2	15		3	15	17	13	8	22	13	9 D

Row labels right side: N O P Q R S T U V W X Y Z

1 N	2	3	4	5	6	7	8	9 D	10	11	12	13 E
14	15	16	17 R	18	19	20	21	22	23	24	25	26

Answer

12	19	1	1	8	21	8	17

201

245 Wordladder

Change one letter at a time (but not the position of any letter) to make a new word – and move from the word at the top of the ladder to the word at the bottom using the exact number of rungs provided.

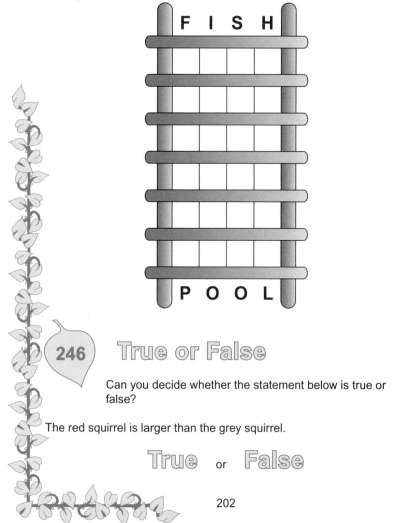

F I S H

P O O L

246 True or False

Can you decide whether the statement below is true or false?

The red squirrel is larger than the grey squirrel.

True or False

202

247 Petal Puzzle

How many words of three or more letters can you make from those on the petals, without using plurals, abbreviations or proper nouns? The central letter must appear once in every word and no letter may be used more than once unless it is on a different petal. There is at least one nine-letter word to be found.

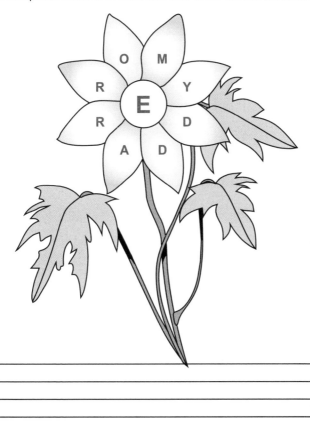

_____

_____

_____

_____

_____

_____

_____

248 Forested Areas

Fit the letters F, O, R, E, S and T into the grid in such a way that each horizontal row, each vertical column and each of the heavily outlined sections of six squares contains a different letter. Some letters are already in place.

			E		F
					S
S					
		T			
	O	R			

249 Fish Tracker

Starting at the top left corner and ending at the bottom right, track a path from letter to letter, in any direction except diagonally, in order to find the hidden fish. All of the letters must be used once only.

T	U	H	A	N	O	V	R	A	S	S	E	P	L	A	I	C
B	R	S	I	C	H	Y	W	G	N	I	R	R	U	B	D	E
O	A	L	F	D	R	O	W	S	N	G	H	E	T	I	A	B
T	S	M	O	N	G	A	R	F	I	T	I	H	W	L	A	R
R	B	E	K	I	P	H	S	I	G	E	O	N	H	A	Y	T
E	M	A	E	R	H	A	O	C	R	U	E	P	T	U	O	R
A	M	C	K	E	L	D	D	K	S	T	R	C	H	C	O	D

250 Anagram Mountain

Correctly solve the anagrams each step of the way from the top to the bottom of the mountain and the name of a marine creature will be revealed in the central column of bricks.

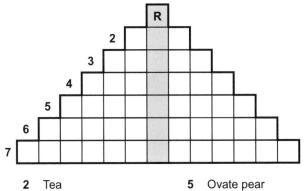

2	Tea	5	Ovate pear
3	Gable	6	Turned on jam
4	Yew hair	7	Mop my clarinet

251 Spelling Bee

Which is the only one of the following to be correctly spelled?

   a   PEREGRIN

   b   PERAGRINE

   c   PEREGRINE

   d   PERREGRIN

Find the correct answer to each question from the four alternatives.

1 On which remote British islands has the largest colony of gannets?
   a. Ailsa Craig   **b.** Sule Stack
   c. St Kilda   **d.** Sula Sgeir

2 What is another name for the 'Monkey Puzzle' tree?
   a. Chile pine   **b.** Peruvian pine
   c. Mexican pine   **d.** California pine

3 Timothy and marram are types of which common plant?
   a. Cress   **b.** Moss
   c. Heather   **d.** Grass

4 The slow worm belongs to which family of animals?
   a. Worms   **b.** Snakes
   c. Beetles   **d.** Lizards

5 Which common plant is also known as ratstail and way-bread?
   a. St John's wort   **b.** Yellow pimpernel
   c. Greater plantain   **d.** Burnet rose

6 Millstone grit is a variety of which kind of stone?
   a. Granite   **b.** Sandstone
   c. Slate   **d.** Chalk

7 Which is the only silk moth normally found in Britain?
   a. Hawk moth   **b.** Emperor moth
   c. Goat moth   **d.** Burnet moth

8 Bee, fly, man and frog are all species of which flowering plant?
   a. Primrose   **b.** Pansy
   c. Orchid   **d.** Anemone

Keyword Crossword

Solve the crossword puzzle in the usual way, then rearrange the letters in the shaded squares to spell out a keyword: the name of a creature.

Across
- **3** Capital of Canada (6)
- **6** Counting frame (6)
- **7** Arch of the foot (6)
- **10** Slip away (6)
- **11** Skin covering the top of the head (5)
- **14** Nautical unit of depth (5)
- **18** Mother superior (6)
- **19** Sacred beetle (6)
- **21** School uniform jacket (6)
- **22** Half asleep (6)

Down
- **1** Stroke tenderly (6)
- **2** Central American republic (6)
- **3** Flexible twig of a willow (5)
- **4** Painting, sculpture, etc (3)
- **5** Venomous snake (3)
- **8** Cliff-dwelling, gull-like bird (4)
- **9** Extremely wicked (4)
- **12** Elegant and stylish (4)
- **13** Animal's den (4)
- **15** Light wind (6)
- **16** Make certain (6)
- **17** Cat with a mottled coat (5)
- **19** Mournful (3)
- **20** In the past (3)

254 Whirlpool

Find a route for the fish to take in order to escape from the middle of the whirlpool to the calmer waters beyond.

255 Plant Sudoku

Every row, every column and each of the nine smaller boxes of nine squares should be filled with a different number from 1 to 9 inclusive. Some numbers are already in place. When the grid is completely filled, decode the numbers in the shaded squares to spell out the name of a plant. Every row should be read from left to right, starting from the top and working to the bottom of the grid.

					4	7		3
				9			8	
		9	3	7				
	6				7	2	3	
7								4
	8	2	6				7	
				3	6	9		
	4			5				
8		3	2					

Code

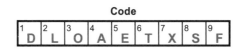

1	2	3	4	5	6	7	8	9
D	L	O	A	E	T	X	S	F

Answer: _____

Shape-up

Every row and column in this grid originally contained one bird, one flower, one leaf, one mushroom and two blank squares, although not necessarily in that order. Every symbol with a black arrow refers to the first of the four symbols encountered in the direction of the arrow. Every symbol with a white arrow refers to the second of the four symbols encountered in the direction of the arrow. Can you complete the original grid?

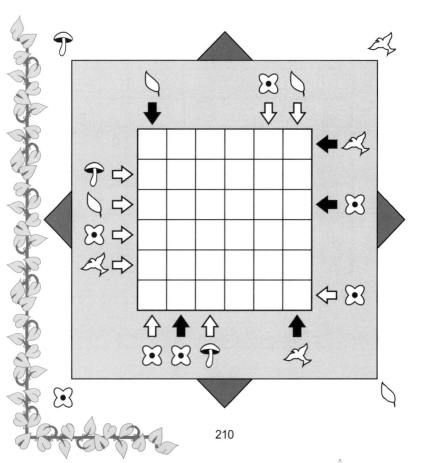

Round Dozen

First solve the clues. All of the solutions end with the letter in the middle of the circle, and in every word an additional letter is in place. When the puzzle is complete, you can then go on to discover an outdoor activity, reading clockwise around the green ring of letters.

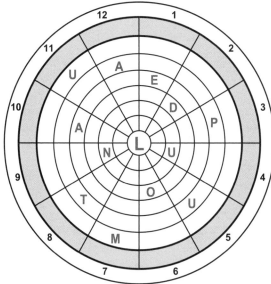

1 Eastern

2 Tending to cure or restore to health

3 Majestic

4 Ultimate

5 Maritime

6 Practising abstention from alcohol

7 Swiss cheese with large holes

8 Outside

9 Sane

10 City formerly known as Constantinople

11 Covering for the kernel of a hard fruit

12 Appreciative

Answer: _____

Natural Selection

Find the correct answer to each question from the four alternatives.

1 What kind of animal is a blood star?
   a. Starfish   **b.** Worm
   c. Bird   **d.** Beetle

2 The pudu is the smallest species of which family of animals?
   a. Goat   **b.** Sheep
   c. Deer   **d.** Horse

3 What do bladderworts, and butterworts have in common?
   a. They only grow on rock   **b.** They only grow in water
   c. They are Britain's only   **d.** All are grey in colour
      insect-eating plants

4 What is a yellow flag?
   a. A butterfly   **b.** A moth
   c. A toad   **d.** An iris

5 What name is given to a very large molehill?
   a. Castle   **b.** Fortress
   c. Tower   **d.** Mole mountain

6 From a species of which plant is laverbread made?
   a. Seaweed   **b.** Nettle
   c. Wheat   **d.** Hops

7 Which one of the following is not a native British woodpecker?
   a. Red crowned   **b.** Great spotted
   c. Green   **d.** Lesser spotted

8 Which of these British wild flowers is protected and must not be picked?
   a. Eyebright   **b.** White campion
   c. Cheddar pink   **d.** Lesser trefoil

259 Pine Forest

The object of this puzzle is to trace a single path from the top left square to the bottom right square of the grid, moving through all of the cells in either a horizontal, vertical or diagonal direction. Every cell must be entered once only and your path should take you through the letters in the sequence P-I-N-E-P-I-N-E, etc. Can you find the logical way through?

P	I	N	E	N	I	P	N
I	P	E	I	P	N	I	E
E	N	P	P	E	I	P	E
I	N	I	P	I	E	N	P
P	E	N	P	N	I	E
N	P	E	I	E	N	I	N
I	N	I	N	N	P	N	I
P	E	I	P	E	E	P	E

260 What's It Worth?

Each symbol stands for a different number. In order to reach the correct total at the end of each row and column, what is the value of the bat, frog, rabbit and starfish?

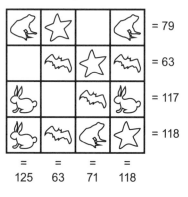

261 Shape Spotter

Which is the only shape to appear twice in exactly the same shading (black, white or green) in the box below? You'll need a keen eye for this one, as some shapes overlap others!

Riddle-Me-Ree

Find one letter per line, following the clues given in the verse below. For example, 'My first is in houses, but never in homes' gives the letter U as the first letter. When you have finished, the letters will spell another word.

My first is in SUMMER, and also in SPRING,

My second's in ROUNDABOUT, and seen in SWING,

My third is in LEAF, as well as in STALK,

My fourth is in LIME, but not found in CHALK,

My fifth is in SINGLET, but never in VEST,

My whole is a creature: some think I'm a pest!

1st	2nd	3rd	4th	5th

263

True or False

Can you decide whether the statement below is true or false?

The pale grey twigs of the ash tree bear pink conical buds.

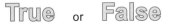

True or False

Telephone Code

Use the telephone dial in order to spell out a quotation attributed to Sir David Attenborough.

6 3 6 6 5 3   5 9 8 8   3 3 3 5   8 4 1 8   8 4 3

6 1 8 9 7 1 5   9 6 7 5 2   4 8   4 5 6 6 7 8 1 6 8

1 6 2   9 1 5 9 1 1 5 3   1 6 2   1 3 1 9 8 4 3 9 5

1 6 2   9 6 6 2 3 7 3 9 5   1 6 2   1 6

1 5 1 0 3 5 3 6 8   1 6 2   1   6 5 3 1 8 9 7 3 .

NNR Arroword

Place the answers in the direction shown by the arrows for each clue. When finished, the letters in the green squares can be rearranged to spell out the name of a National Nature Reserve in Dorset.

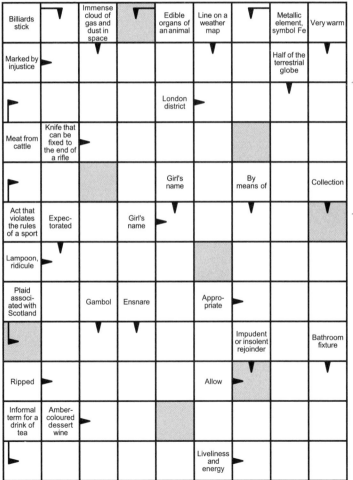

Billiards stick	▼	Immense cloud of gas and dust in space	▼	Edible organs of an animal	Line on a weather map	▼	Metallic element, symbol Fe	Very warm
Marked by injustice ►		▼			▼		Half of the terrestrial globe	▼
⚑				London district ►		▼		
Meat from cattle	Knife that can be fixed to the end of a rifle ►							
⚑				Girl's name		By means of		Collection
Act that violates the rules of a sport	Expec-torated		Girl's name ►	▼		▼		▼
Lampoon, ridicule ►	▼							
Plaid associated with Scotland		Gambol	Ensnare		Appro-priate ►			
⚑		▼	▼			Impudent or insolent rejoinder		Bathroom fixture
Ripped ►					Allow	▼		▼
Informal term for a drink of tea	Amber-coloured dessert wine ►							
⚑					Liveliness and energy ►			

217

Mix 'n' Match

Pair up each of the boxes below to form the names of
eight different flowers.

RBUR

SUN

BUTTE

MONE

COW

BELL

FOOT

ONY

COLTS

GLOVE

BET

SLIP

ANE

DEW

FOX

HARE

218

267 Round the Block

You won't need a starting block to get you under way, because it isn't a race! Just arrange the six-letter solutions to the clues into the six blocks around each clue number. Write the answers in a clockwise or anticlockwise direction and you'll find that the last answer fits into the first; the main problem will be to decide in which square to put the first letter of each word…

When read in a clockwise direction (not necessarily starting at either of the topmost squares), the letters in the pale green squares spell out the name of an insect.

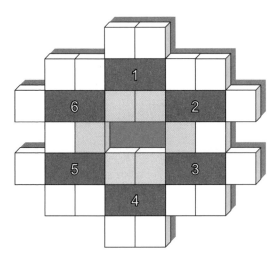

1 Spiny plant of desert regions

2 Loose-fitting garments

3 Underground passageway

4 Nocturnal wildcat of Central and South America

5 Mystic, supernatural

6 Ornamental plaster applied to exterior walls

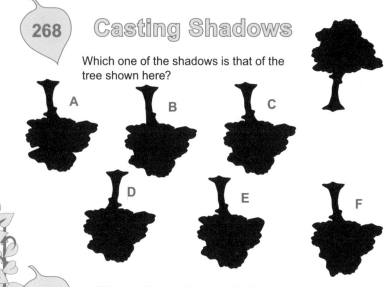

268 Casting Shadows

Which one of the shadows is that of the tree shown here?

A

B

C

D

E

F

269 The Bottom Line

The bottom line of this grid is waiting to be filled. Every square in the solution contains only one symbol from rows 1 to 4 above, although two or more squares in the solution may contain the same symbol. At the end of every numbered row is a score, which shows:

1 the number of symbols placed in the correct finishing position on the bottom line, as indicated by a tick; and

2 the number of symbols which appear on the bottom line, but in a different position, as indicated by a cross.

Can you fill each square with the correct symbol?

				Score
1				X X
2				X X
3				X X X
4				X X
				✓✓✓✓

Solutions

1

Answer: ARDINGLY

2

3

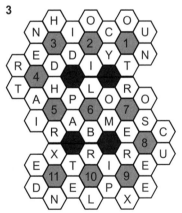

Answer: BIRCH

4

Answer: MONARCH

5

Here is one possible solution: FISH, fist, list, lost, loot, foot, fool, FOWL

6

False: It was introduced. The Hazel Dormouse is native.

7

The nine-letter word is: CARNIVORE

Solutions

8

T	F	O	S	E	R
R	S	F	O	T	E
E	R	T	F	S	O
F	E	R	T	O	S
S	O	E	R	F	T
O	T	S	E	R	F

9

Chipmunk, rabbit, giraffe, hippopotamus, squirrel, bear, fox, kangaroo, lemur, deer, gerbil, mouse, aardvark, weasel, tiger, lynx, camel, otter, hyena, horse.

10

2 Act, 3 Ether, 4 Patient,
5 Taxidermy, 6 Acupuncture,
7 Accompaniment.
Answer: ECHIDNA

11

The correctly spelled word is: c

12

1 b, 2 c, 3 a, 4 d, 5 b, 6 a, 7 b,
8 d.

13

G	A	R	B	O		S	H	E	E	P
	D		R			U		D		R
M	O	L	A	R		S	A	U	C	E
	R		S			P		C		T
M	E	A	S	U	R	E		A	C	E
E		V		S		C		T		X
R	O	E		E	N	T	R	E	A	T
M		R		L			O		G	
A	B	A	T	E		W	O	M	A	N
I		G		S			S		I	
D	R	E	S	S		A	T	O	N	E

Answer: BADGER

14

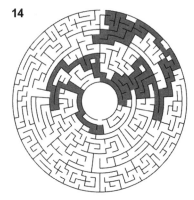

Solutions

15

2	5	9	8	1	6	7	3	4
6	7	3	9	4	5	2	8	1
8	1	4	2	7	3	9	6	5
7	3	2	4	8	9	5	1	6
1	6	5	7	3	2	4	9	8
4	9	8	5	6	1	3	2	7
3	4	7	1	9	8	6	5	2
9	2	1	6	5	4	8	7	3
5	8	6	3	2	7	1	4	9

Answer: CAIRNGORMS

18

1 a, 2 c, 3 d, 4 c, 5 b, 6 d, 7 a, 8 b.

19

16

17

1 Merchant, 2 Argument,
3 Greatest, 4 Prospect,
5 Incident, 6 Eyesight,
7 Gradient, 8 Redolent,
9 Occupant, 10 Undercut,
11 Sergeant, 12 Eggplant.
Answer: MAGPIE and GROUSE

20

Bat = 3, frog = 6, rabbit = 4 and starfish = 9.

21

22

RIVER

23

True.

24

"It is not the strongest of the species that survives, nor the most intelligent that survives. It is the one that is the most adaptable to change."

223

Solutions

25

	T		A			V		W
T	R	A	N	S	P	I	R	E
	O		I			S		E
N	U	R	S	E	M	A	I	D
	T	H	E	R	E		N	
		E		A	M	P	L	E
S	P	A			O	R	A	L
	R		P			O	W	L
C	O	V	E	R	U	P		I
	S	A	G	O		A	S	P
P	E	N		P	A	N	T	S
	E	R	E		E	Y	E	

Answer: ROSEMOOR

26

Birch, blackthorn, hornbeam, plane, poplar, sycamore, walnut, willow.

27

1 Bowing (a), 2 Ginger (c),
3 Grange (c), 4 Orange (a),
5 Origin (c), 6 Owning (c).
Answer: WIGEON

28

E

29

30

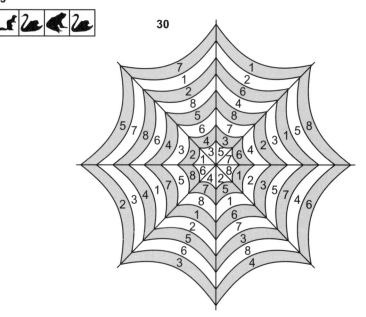

Solutions

31

Answer: ANNAPURNA

32

33

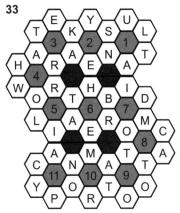

Answer: HEATHER

34

Answer: SOAPWORT

35

Here is one possible solution: BIRD, bind, bend, bent, best, NEST

36

True.

37

The nine-letter word is: PACHYDERM

Solutions

38

T	S	R	E	F	O
F	O	E	T	S	R
R	T	S	O	E	F
E	F	T	R	O	S
O	R	F	S	T	E
S	E	O	F	R	T

39

Mountain, prairie, hill, desert, spring, gorge, waterfall, tundra, river, stream, swamp, volcano, plateau, moor, valley, plain, estuary, geyser, fissure, sea.

40

2 Ant, 3 Inert, 4 Hammock,
5 Osteopath, 6 Responsible,
7 Unforgettable.
Answer: ANEMONE

41

The correctly spelled word is: d

42

1 b, 2 d, 3 c, 4 a, 5 b, 6 d, 7 a,
8 c.

43

Answer: SQUIRREL

44

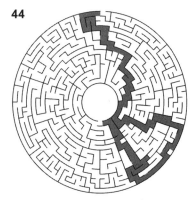

Solutions

45

9	5	1	4	7	8	2	3	6
4	8	6	2	3	5	9	7	1
3	2	7	1	6	9	5	4	8
1	7	4	6	9	3	8	5	2
8	3	2	5	1	4	7	6	9
6	9	5	8	2	7	4	1	3
2	1	9	7	4	6	3	8	5
5	4	3	9	8	1	6	2	7
7	6	8	3	5	2	1	9	4

Answer: MONKSHOOD

48

1 a, 2 b, 3 d, 4 a, 5 c, 6 a, 7 c, 8 b.

49

46

47

1 Explicit, 2 Abundant,
3 Resident, 4 Weirdest,
5 Ignorant, 6 Gradient,
7 Beetroot, 8 Elephant,
9 Earliest, 10 Tolerant,
11 Lifeboat, 12 Escargot.
Answer: EARWIG and BEETLE

50

Bat = 11, frog = 10,
rabbit = 9 and starfish = 7.

51

52

BEECH

53

True.

54

"It is experimentally known that birds do not instinctively know the duration of their own incubation."

Solutions

55

	D		B			C		B
P	E	N	I	N	S	U	L	A
	C		D			B		T
G	O	V	E	R	N	E	S	S
	R	A	T	I	O		P	
		S		P	A	P	U	A
A	C	T			H	Y	M	N
	H		B			J	E	T
N	A	M	I	B	I	A		H
	S	A	N	E		M	A	R
D	E	N		N	Y	A	L	A
		E	A	T		S	E	X

Answer: TAYNISH

56

Bistort, campion, centaury, clover, heather, mallow, orpine, poppy.

57

1 Heater (a), 2 Stream (c), 3 Rabbit (a), 4 Banana (a/c), 5 Tehran (a), 6 Throne (a). Answer: ANTHER

58

D

59

60

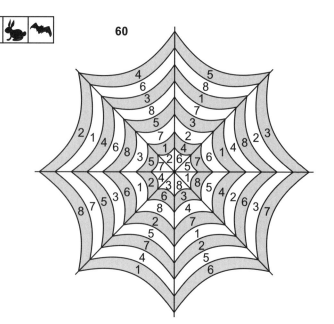

Solutions

61

Answer: TADPOLES

62

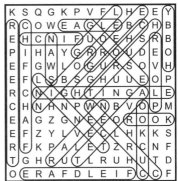

63

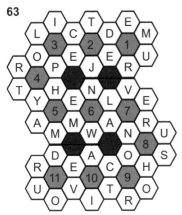

Answer: DARTMOOR

64

Answer: STARFISH

65

Here is one possible solution:
PINE, fine, find, fend, feed,
fled, flee, free, TREE

66

False: Britain's
smallest bird is the
goldcrest.

67

The nine-letter
word is:
DANDELION

68

S	O	R	E	T	F
F	T	O	R	E	S
E	F	S	O	R	T
T	S	E	F	O	R
R	E	F	T	S	O
O	R	T	S	F	E

69

Mayfly, dragonfly, cricket, cockroach, beetle, earwig, millipede, louse, stonefly, alderfly, ant, flea, springtail, centipede, thrip, lacewing, bee, tick.

70

2 Who, 3 Brush, 4 Blanket, 5 Roundworm, 6 Displeasure, 7 Appropriately.
Answer: THUNDER

71

The correctly spelled word is: b

72

1 b, 2 c, 3 d, 4 a, 5 b, 6 a, 7 c, 8 b.

73

Answer: OTTER

74

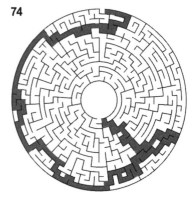

Solutions

75

1	4	7	6	2	9	8	5	3
8	5	3	4	7	1	2	6	9
9	6	2	5	8	3	1	7	4
7	8	9	3	5	2	6	4	1
5	3	6	8	1	4	9	2	7
4	2	1	9	6	7	5	3	8
3	9	5	2	4	8	7	1	6
6	1	4	7	9	5	3	8	2
2	7	8	1	3	6	4	9	5

Answer: ELDERBERRY

78

1 a, 2 c, 3 d, 4 a, 5 c, 6 a, 7 b, 8 b.

79

76

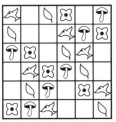

77

1 Sapphire, 2 Particle,
3 Rehearse, 4 Ultimate,
5 Camomile, 6 Emigrate,
7 Windpipe, 8 Immature,
9 Lemonade, 10 Loophole,
11 Omnivore, 12 Wardrobe.
Answer: SPRUCE and WILLOW

80

Bat = 14, frog = 10,
rabbit = 12 and starfish = 16.

81

82

HEDGE

83

True.

84

"Did Saint Francis preach to the birds? Whatever for? If he really liked birds he would have done better to preach to the cats."

Solutions

85

	D		S		D		A	
M	I	S	C	H	I	E	F	
	P	E	A		R	A	T	E
	L	A	N	C	E	R		A
T	O	M		H		W	A	R
	M		B	E	N	I	G	N
M	A	C	A	W		G	A	S
	T		T		B		R	
		S	H	O	U	T		B
S	A	L	E		G	U	R	U
	D	A	R	E		N	A	N
L	O	T	S		H	A	W	K

Answer: STIPERSTONES

86

Blewit, blusher, boletus, deceiver, grisette, puffball, truffle, tinder.

87

1 Potato (a), 2 Police (a), 3 Holier (c), 4 Honest (a), 5 Nerves (c), 6 Staple (a). Answer: STOLON

88

A

89

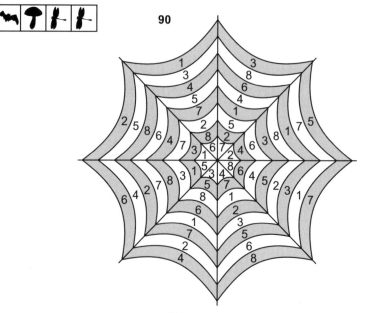

90

232

Solutions

91

Answer: RUCKSACK

92

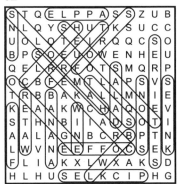

93

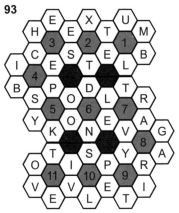

Answer: MENDIPS

94

Answer: LADYBIRD

95

Here is one possible solution: TICK, tics, ties, tees, fees, feed, fled, FLEA

96

True.

97

The nine-letter word is: WATERFALL

Solutions

98

R	E	T	F	O	S
S	R	E	O	F	T
T	F	S	R	E	O
O	T	R	E	S	F
F	S	O	T	R	E
E	O	F	S	T	R

99

Fluorite, barite, quartz, amethyst, calcite, amber, garnet, jet, serpentine, agate, marble, selenite, jasper, limestone, sandstone, granite, flint, slate.

100

2 Arc, 3 Snare, 4 Pitcher, 5 Blackmail, 6 Discrepancy, 7 Argumentative.
Answer: BRACKEN

101

The correctly spelled word is: a

102

1 c, 2 a, 3 c, 4 d, 5 b, 6 d, 7 a, 8 c.

103

Answer: HEDGEHOG

104

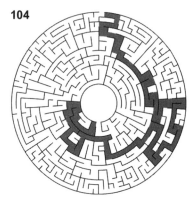

Solutions

105

6	4	2	1	8	7	9	5	3
9	8	7	5	2	3	6	4	1
1	5	3	9	6	4	2	8	7
8	9	5	7	3	2	4	1	6
2	1	4	6	5	8	7	3	9
7	3	6	4	1	9	5	2	8
5	2	8	3	7	6	1	9	4
3	7	9	2	4	1	8	6	5
4	6	1	8	9	5	3	7	2

Answer: COLTSFOOT

108

1 d, 2 a, 3 c, 4 b, 5 d, 6 b, 7 b, 8 d.

109

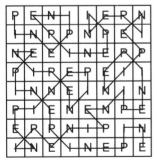

106

107

1 Calendar, 2 Ancestor,
3 Peculiar, 4 Engineer,
5 Radiator, 6 Cavalier,
7 Abattoir, 8 Inferior, 9 Lavender,
10 Lecturer, 11 Interior,
12 Explorer.
Answer: CAPERCAILLIE

110

Bat = 18, frog = 31,
rabbit = 22 and starfish = 27.

111

112

MIDGE

113

False: It is the smallest of all the fur seals.

114

"Nothing in the nature around us is evil. This needs to be repeated since one of the human ways of talking oneself into inhuman acts is to cite the supposed cruelty of nature."

115

	F		F	E		
G	O	R	I	L	L	A	A
	W			O	A	S	I	S
C	L	O	S	E	N	E	S	S
		W			E		L
F	L	E	S	H		H	E	R
	A		C	A	F	E		A
B	Y	T	E	S		N	U	N
	E		N		S		P
F	R	E	E		W	E	P	T
		B	R	O	A	D	E	R
B	A	B	Y		G	O	R	Y

Answer: DENGIE

116

Lapwing, moorhen, plover, pochard, shelduck, turnstone, warbler, woodcock.

117

1 Tallow (c), 2 Animal (a), 3 Iguana (c), 4 Frugal (c), 5 French (a), 6 Stolen (c).
Answer: LAUREL

118

C

119

120

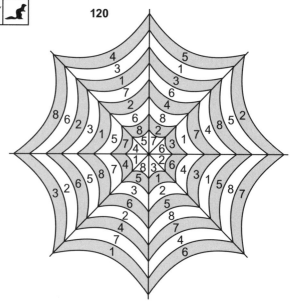

236

Solutions

121

Answer: SAHARA

122

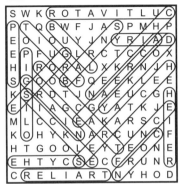

123

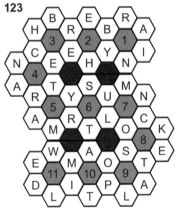

Answer: WINTER

124

Answer: PERIWINKLE

125

Here is one possible
solution: FROG, flog, clog,
clod, clad, glad, goad, TOAD

126

False: A female
polecat is known as
a 'jill'.

127

The nine-letter
word is:
WHITEBEAM

128

R	E	S	T	O	F
F	S	O	E	R	T
O	R	T	S	F	E
T	F	E	O	S	R
S	T	R	F	E	O
E	O	F	R	T	S

129

Farrier, ploughman, carter, gamekeeper, weaver, farmer, milkmaid, fisherman, miller, forester, shepherd, dairyman, swineherd, wheelwright, thatcher.

130

2 Dog, 3 Large, 4 Granted, 5 Certainly, 6 Bewildering, 7 Ornithologist.
Answer: TORNADO

131

The correctly spelled word is: b

132

1 c, 2 c, 3 b, 4 d, 5 a, 6 d, 7 c, 8 a.

133

Answer: SHREW

134

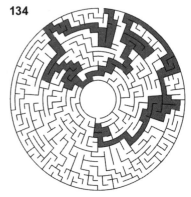

Solutions

135

2	9	5	3	8	4	1	6	7
8	6	7	9	2	1	5	4	3
1	4	3	6	7	5	2	9	8
4	1	8	2	9	3	6	7	5
3	2	6	8	5	7	4	1	9
7	5	9	1	4	6	3	8	2
5	3	4	7	1	9	8	2	6
6	7	2	4	3	8	9	5	1
9	8	1	5	6	2	7	3	4

Answer: CHEVIOTS

138

1 b, 2 d, 3 a, 4 c, 5 c, 6 a, 7 b, 8 d.

139

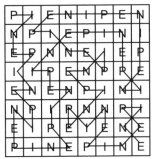

136

137

1 Yosemite, 2 Employee,
3 Lacrosse, 4 Levitate,
5 Obstacle, 6 Wreckage,
7 Hardware, 8 Activate,
9 Marriage, 10 Memorise,
11 Envelope, 12 Resonate.
Answer: YELLOWHAMMER

140

Bat = 17, frog = 18,
rabbit = 20 and starfish = 14.

141

142

DITCH

143

True.

144

"Forests, lakes, and rivers, clouds and winds, stars and flowers, stupendous glaciers and crystal snowflakes – every form of animate or inanimate existence, leaves its impress upon the soul of man."

239

Solutions

145

		G				D	
B	I	E	R		A	P	E	X
	O	V	E	R	D	U	E	
	T	E	A		A	L	M	S
B	A	N	T	A	M	S		O
		T			S	E	A	L
L	A	S	S	O			W	
	C		T	H	O	R	N	S
S	I	N	A	I		A		C
	D		T	O	U	P	E	E
L	I	E	U		S	I	G	N
	C		S	L	E	D	G	E

Answer: MURLOUGH

146

Alder, beech, hawthorn, hemlock, juniper, laurel, plane, rowan.

147

1 Stolen (c), 2 Devote (c), 3 Sleeve (c), 4 Peered (a), 5 Pamper (a), 6 Parcel (c). Answer: PLOVER

148

F

149

150

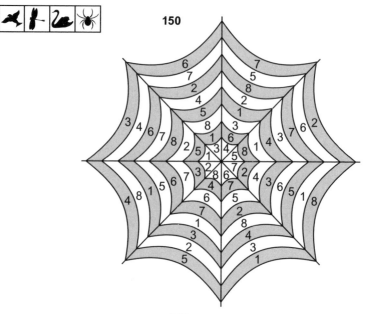

151

Answer: SONORAN

152

153

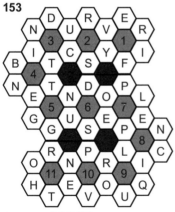

Answer: GORSE

154

Answer: NUTHATCH

155

Here is one possible solution:
TREE, free, flee, fled, feed,
heed, hoed, hood, WOOD

156

False: It has
five white
petals.

157

The nine-letter
word is:
PIMPERNEL

Solutions

158

F	T	O	S	R	E
O	E	S	R	F	T
E	F	R	O	T	S
T	S	E	F	O	R
S	R	F	T	E	O
R	O	T	E	S	F

159

Python, chameleon, anaconda, mamba, toad, iguana, salamander, tortoise, cobra, gecko, krait, turtle, alligator, crocodile, terrapin, newt, skink, asp, frog.

160

2 Bad, 3 Ample, 4 Slowest,
5 Abominate, 6 Misconstrue,
7 Choreographer.
Answer: LAPWING

161

The correctly spelled word is: c

162

1 a, 2 b, 3 c, 4 a, 5 d, 6 c, 7 b,
8 c.

163

C	O	M	M	A		B	R	I	E	F
	P		E			O		T		A
V	E	R	T	I	G	O		A	I	L
	R		R			K		L		L
C	A	K	E	D		L	Y	I	N	G
A		I		O	R	E		C		U
R	E	N	A	L		T	A	S	T	Y
A		G		P			G		O	
W	E	D		H	E	A	R	S	A	Y
A		O		I			E		S	
Y	E	M	E	N		B	E	R	T	H

Answer: DORMOUSE

164

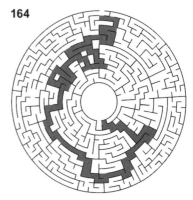

242

Solutions

165

9	3	4	5	1	2	7	6	8
1	5	2	6	7	8	4	3	9
6	8	7	4	9	3	5	1	2
7	2	6	8	5	9	3	4	1
3	9	5	7	4	1	8	2	6
4	1	8	2	3	6	9	7	5
2	6	9	3	8	7	1	5	4
8	4	3	1	6	5	2	9	7
5	7	1	9	2	4	6	8	3

Answer: FEVERFEW

166

167

1 Backward, 2 Emulated,
3 Waveband, 4 Included,
5 Captured, 6 Knighted,
7 Thailand, 8 Utilised,
9 Released, 10 Narrated,
11 Expected, 12 Resolved.
Answer: BEWICK and TURNER

168

1 d, 2 a, 3 a, 4 a, 5 d, 6 c, 7 b,
8 b.

169

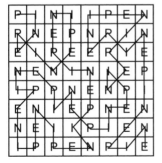

170

Bat = 8, frog = 11, rabbit = 9 and
starfish = 10.

171

172

CIDER

173

True.

174

"Everybody needs beauty as well as bread, places
to play in and pray in, where nature may heal and
give strength to body and soul."

Solutions

175

	T		A		C		M	
	A	M	B	R	O	S	I	A
	L	O	U		M		L	
S	C	O	T	S	P	I	N	E
		S		L	A	M	E	D
	F	E	D	O	R	A		I
	R			E	I	G	H	T
C	O	P	E		S	E	A	S
		A			O		W	
I	N	S	O	M	N	I	A	C
	O	S	L	O		R	I	O
	R	E	D	O		K	I	N

Answer: DUNGENESS

176

Celandine, daisy, dandelion, hepatica, hogweed, mayweed, primrose, yarrow.

177

1 Ninety (c), 2 Trilby (c),
3 Albert (a), 4 Easter (c),
5 Oddest (a), 6 Adonis (a).
Answer: BETONY

178

B

179

180

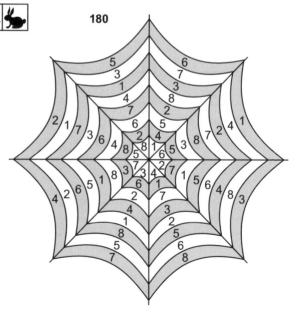

Solutions

181

Answer: HUMBER

182

183

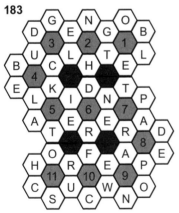

Answer: PIGEON

184

Answer: HONEYSUCKLE

185

Here is one possible solution: LEAF, deaf, dead, deed, seed, seem, STEM

186

True.

187

The nine-letter word is: BUTTERCUP

Solutions

188

S	E	R	O	T	F
F	O	R	E	S	T
T	S	O	F	E	R
O	T	S	R	F	E
R	E	F	T	O	S
E	F	T	S	R	O

189

Leopard, plume, tiger, hawk, emperor, goat, forester, cinnabar, puss, burnet, magpie, lobster, vapourer, plusia, ghost, longhorn, ermine, thorn, pug, footman.

190

2 Act, 3 Petal, 4 Ignored, 5 Recapture, 6 Inexcusable, 7 Procrastinate.
Answer: OCTOPUS

191

The correctly spelled word is: a

192

1 a, 2 d, 3 d, 4 d, 5 a, 6 b, 7 d, 8 c.

193

Answer: SALMON

194

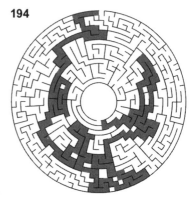

Solutions

195

4	6	3	7	5	2	8	9	1
1	7	2	6	8	9	4	3	5
5	9	8	4	3	1	7	2	6
3	8	9	1	2	7	5	6	4
7	1	5	3	6	4	9	8	2
6	2	4	8	9	5	3	1	7
8	4	1	2	7	3	6	5	9
2	5	6	9	4	8	1	7	3
9	3	7	5	1	6	2	4	8

Answer: PENNINES

198

1 b, 2 d, 3 c, 4 a, 5 d, 6 a, 7 d, 8 c.

199

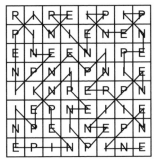

196

197

1 Nonsense, 2 Eligible,
3 Tentacle, 4 Triangle,
5 Lingerie, 6 Encircle, 7 Tolerate,
8 Exposure, 9 Adelaide,
10 Surprise, 11 Embezzle,
12 Language.
Answer: NETTLE and TEASEL

200

Bat = 12, frog = 14,
rabbit = 13 and starfish = 15.

201

202

SHEEP

203

True.

204

"Bats drink on the wing, like swallows, by sipping the surface, as they play over pools and streams."

247

Solutions

205

	A			A		S		
	S	C	A	R		T	I	C
	B	A	C	K	E	R		R
D	O	M	E			A	W	E
		B	R	E	A	T	H	E
		R		X		O	I	L
S	W	I	F	T	E	S	T	
	A	C	R	E		P	E	A
	L		A	R	C	H		R
F	L	Y	N	N		E	V	E
	E		C	A	R	R	O	T
S	T	E	E	L		E	W	E

Answer: FORVIE

206

Buzzard, goshawk, kestrel, nuthatch, redstart, skylark, starling, swallow.

207

1 Kitten (a), 2 Thwart (c),
3 Scarab (a), 4 Baboon (a),
5 Ribbon (c), 6 Bikini (c).
Answer: RABBIT

208

D

209

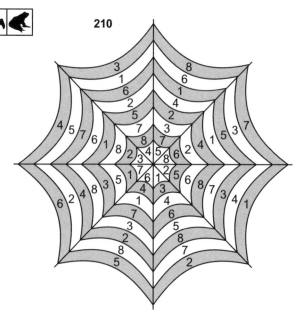

210

Solutions

211

Answer: HAWTHORN

212

213

Answer: EXMOOR

214

Answer: FOXGLOVE

215

Here is one possible solution: POND, fond, bond, band, land, lane LAKE

216

False: It twines spirally clockwise.

217

The nine-letter word is: CELANDINE

Solutions

218

E	R	S	T	O	F
F	S	E	R	T	O
O	T	F	S	R	E
S	O	R	F	E	T
R	E	T	O	F	S
T	F	O	E	S	R

219

Thrush, blackbird, redstart, fieldfare, bluetit, chaffinch, greenfinch, dove, cuckoo, goose, swan, magpie, rook, grouse, partridge, heron, eagle, goshawk.

220

2 Bad, 3 Shine, 4 Younger, 5 Overboard, 6 Redecorated, 7 Scriptwriters.
Answer: RAINBOW

221

The correctly spelled word is: d

222

1 b, 2 c, 3 d, 4 d, 5 a, 6 d, 7 c, 8 a.

223

Answer: TERMITE

224

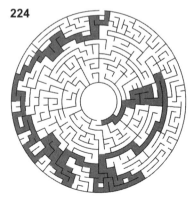

Solutions

225

4	6	1	2	9	7	3	5	8
2	5	9	3	6	8	7	4	1
8	7	3	1	4	5	2	6	9
5	9	4	6	2	3	1	8	7
6	1	7	5	8	9	4	2	3
3	2	8	4	7	1	6	9	5
7	4	5	9	1	6	8	3	2
1	3	6	8	5	2	9	7	4
9	8	2	7	3	4	5	1	6

Answer: SNOWDROP

226

227

1 Hazelnut, 2 Outsmart,
3 Upmarket, 4 Novelist,
5 Diligent, 6 Somerset,
7 Transmit, 8 Obedient,
9 Noisiest, 10 Gauntlet,
11 Unspoilt, 12 Exorcist.
Answer: HOUNDSTONGUE

228

1 b, 2 d, 3 a, 4 c, 5 b, 6 d, 7 a,
8 d.

229

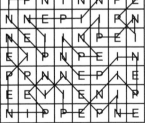

230

Bat = 18, frog = 13,
rabbit = 10 and starfish = 12.

231

232

WHELK

233

False: About
2.5 per cent
are marine.

234

"The pigeon here is a beautiful bird, of a delicate
bronze colour, tinged with pink about the neck,
and the wings marked with green and purple."

Solutions

235

	U			A			H	
	P	L	A	C	A	T	E	
	S	E	C	T		E	L	F
	E	C	H	O		S	P	A
O	T	T	E	R		T		D
		U			L	A	Y	S
	C	R	E	M	A	T	E	
N	O	E	L		M	E	S	H
	R		S		B			I
	P	E	E	P		O	A	K
U	S	A		A	D	A	G	E
		R	A	T		F	O	R

Answer: BENACRE

236

Aspen, chestnut, cypress, hazel, larch, maple, redwood, spindle.

237

1 Weevil (a), 2 Jewels (a),
3 Leaves (a), 4 Savage (c),
5 Desert (c), 6 Failed (c).
Answer: WEASEL

238

E

239

240

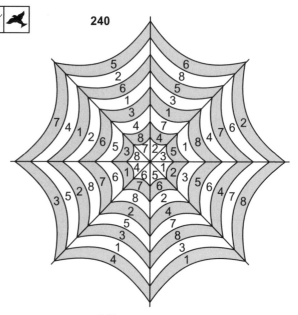

Solutions

241

Answer: RIDDON

242

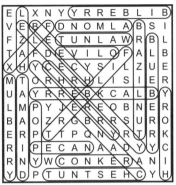

243

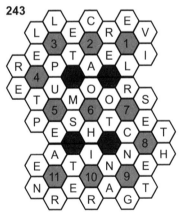

Answer: SPRING

244

Answer: CINNABAR

245

Here is one possible solution: FISH, wish, wise, wile, pile, pole, poll, POOL

246

False: The grey squirrel is larger than the red squirrel.

247

The nine-letter word is: DROMEDARY

Solutions

248

O	R	S	E	T	F
T	E	O	F	R	S
S	F	E	T	O	R
E	S	T	R	F	O
R	T	F	O	S	E
F	O	R	S	E	T

249

Turbot, salmon, garfish, pike, bream, mackerel, haddock, sturgeon, halibut, whiting, herring, swordfish, anchovy, wrasse, plaice, dab, ray, trout, perch, cod.

250

2 Eat, 3 Bagel, 4 Haywire, 5 Evaporate, 6 Adjournment, 7 Complimentary.
Answer: RAGWORM

251

The correctly spelled word is: c

252

1 c, 2 a, 3 d, 4 d, 5 c, 6 b, 7 b, 8 c.

253

Answer: POLECAT

254

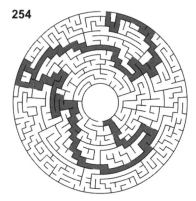

255

5	2	8	1	6	4	7	9	3
3	7	4	5	9	2	1	8	6
6	1	9	3	7	8	4	2	5
9	6	5	4	8	7	2	3	1
7	3	1	9	2	5	8	6	4
4	8	2	6	1	3	5	7	9
1	5	7	8	3	6	9	4	2
2	4	6	7	5	9	3	1	8
8	9	3	2	4	1	6	5	7

Answer: TOADFLAX

258

1 a, 2 c, 3 c, 4 d, 5 b, 6 a, 7 a, 8 c.

259

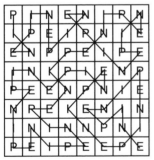

256

257

1 Oriental, 2 Remedial,
3 Imperial, 4 Eventual,
5 Nautical, 6 Teetotal,
7 Emmental, 8 External,
9 Rational, 10 Istanbul,
11 Nutshell, 12 Grateful.
Answer: ORIENTEERING

260

Bat = 23, frog = 31,
rabbit = 47 and starfish = 17.

261

262

SNAIL

263

False: They bear black conical buds.

264

"People must feel that the natural world is important and valuable and beautiful and wonderful and an amazement and a pleasure."

Solutions

265

	C		O			I		
	U	N	F	A	I	R		H
B	E	E	F		S	O	H	O
		B	A	Y	O	N	E	T
F	O	U	L		B		M	
		L		M	A	V	I	S
	S	A	T	I	R	I	S	E
	P			R		A	P	T
T	A	R	T	A	N		H	
	T	O	R	N		L	E	T
		M	A	D	E	I	R	A
C	U	P	P	A		P	E	P

Answer: DURLSTON

266

Anemone, betony, butterbur, coltsfoot, cowslip, foxglove, harebell, sundew.

267

1 Cactus (c), 2 Tunics (a), 3 Tunnel (c), 4 Ocelot (a), 5 Occult (a), 6 Stucco (c). Answer: LOCUST

268

C

269